D1447653

ARDNAMURCHAN

a guide to geological excursions

Department of Geology, University of Glasgow

E. M. DURRANCE

Department of Geology, University of Exeter

and

J. N. WALSH

Department of Geology, King's College, London

Edinburgh Geological Society

Edinburgh Geological Society
c/o Grant Institute of Geology
West Mains Road, Edinburgh, EH9 3JW

ISBN 0 904440 02 8

£2.00

Printed in Great Britain by
Lindsay & Co. Ltd., Edinburgh

This guide is dedicated
to the memory of
Dr J. E. RICHEY, F.R.S.

Users of this guide in the field are requested to always bear in mind the various points made in the geological code of conduct published in 1975 by The Geologists' Association. Copies of this code are available from The Librarian, The Geologists' Association, c/o Department of Geology, University College, Gower Street, London, WC1E 6BT. Organisers of field parties should note the general unsuitability of the roads in Ardnamurchan for large coaches and also check in advance the times of crossing of the Corran ferry near Ballachulish.

Cover photograph: Aerial Mosaic of Ardnamurchan showing the most complete set of ring intrusions in the British Isles. The relief of the hills is seen more clearly if the book is turned upside down, that is, viewed from the north.

Foreword

The compilation of a field guide presents several difficulties. If it is too long, accounts of rocks or rock suites tend to be difficult to find and the price is too high; and yet, if certain rock types are left out, the guide will fail in its purpose. Therefore I have tried, with the help of my co-authors, to follow an intermediate course: each rock type is dealt with and extended descriptions are given of those rocks which have received attention from research workers in the recent past. Recent ideas on the form and structure of Tertiary igneous centres have been included and an attempt made to outline some of the problems still requiring solution. In the excursion descriptions we have tried to make these as detailed as possible both in location finding and geology, so that the geology can be followed in the field with reasonable ease.

C. D. Gribble
April 1976

v

Acknowledgements

I wish to thank my co-authors, Eric Durrance and Nick Walsh, for their splendid accounts of Centres 2 and 3 respectively; and also for trying to follow my many and mostly incomprehensible instructions. My thanks to the Edinburgh Geological Society for continuing to produce an Ardnamurchan guide, and especially to Norman Butcher and Walter Mykura of the Society for their help in many aspects of the organisation. I am grateful to the Assistant Director of the Institute of Geological Sciences, Edinburgh, for permission to use many of Richey's diagrams, and particularly to Robert Ramsay of the I.G.S. for drawing the marvellous colour map and all the diagrams in the text. The map is based on Crown Copyright Geological Survey maps, reproduced by permission of the Controller of Her Majesty's Stationery Office. I am also grateful to Ian Vann and Kenneth MacDonald for contributing the sections on dykes and Ardnamurchan place names respectively, Walter Mykura who helped referee the original text, and Michael Keen for his assistance with the Mesozoic rocks. All of us thank the various secretaries involved, and particularly Dorothy Oliver who typed the final, complete manuscript. We all acknowledge financial assistance from our respective universities, Glasgow, Exeter and King's College (Central Research Fund), which supported the fieldwork required in the preparation of this guide. Finally, I should like to thank the Carnegie Trust for a substantial grant towards publication costs of the coloured map.

C. D. Gribble
April 1976

CONTENTS

page

Introduction   1

The Moine country rocks   9

Mesozoic sedimentary rocks   9

Tertiary igneous rocks   12

   Basalt lava flows   12

   Centre 1   13

      Vent rocks (and associated extrusive rocks)
         Pitchstone lavas   17
         Trachyte lavas   17

      Intrusive rocks (plutonic and hypabyssal types)
         Gabbro of Meall nan Con   18
         Quartz-gabbro of Faskadale   18
         Granophyre of Faskadale   19
         The dolerites
            Porphyritic dolerite   20
            Quartz-dolerite of Camphouse   21
            Augite-diorite of Camphouse   21
            Beinn an Leathaid dolerite   21
            Ben Hiant dolerite   22

Centre 2   25

   Vent rocks   25

   Intrusive plutonic rocks
      Hypersthene-gabbro of Ardnamurchan Point   28
      Older gabbro of Lochan an Aodainn   36
      Quartz-gabbro of Garbh-dhail   37
      Granophyre of Grigadale   37
      Older quartz-gabbro of Beinn Bhuidhe   38
      Quartz-gabbro of Aodann   39
      Granophyric quartz-dolerite of Sgùrr nam
         Meann   39
      Eucrite of Beinn nan Ord   43
      Quartz-gabbros of Loch Caorach and Beinn na
         Seilg   44
      Younger quartz-gabbro of Beinn Bhuidhe   45
      Fluxion gabbro of Portuairk   46
      Aodann felsite   46

The acid and basic magmas of Ardnamurchan   47

The cone-sheets of Centres 1, 2 and 3   48

Centre 3   53

   Intrusive plutonic rocks
      Quartz-gabbro of Faskadale   55
      Fluxion gabbro of Faskadale   55
      Gabbro of Plocaig   57
      Porphyritic gabbro of Meall nan Con screen   57
      Great Eucrite   57

Biotite-eucrite and inner eucrite   58
Quartz-gabbro of Meall an Tarmachain
     summit   59
Quartz-dolerite veined with granophyre   59
Quartz-gabbros   60
Fluxion gabbro of Glendrian   61
Fluxion gabbro of Sìthean Mór   61
Tonalite and quartz-monzonite   62

The structure of Centre 3 and the importance
     of fluxion structures in the gabbros   63

The petrogenesis of the rocks of Centre 3   65

References   68

Excursions

Excursion 1: Ormsaigbeg to Mingary Castle
     (sections A, B and C)   72
Excursion 2: Kilchoan, Beinn na Seilg and
     Aodann (sections A and B)   82
Excursion 3: Portuairk, Lighthouse and
     Achosnich (sections A and B)   91
Excursion 4: Sanna Bay to Rubha Carrach   101
Excursion 5: Ben (or Beinn) Hiant   106
Excursion 6: The augite-diorite of Camphouse
     and Faskadale Bay (sections A and B)   109
Excursion 7: Ring intrusions of Centre 3   115

Appendix   Glossary of Ardnamurchan place names   118

INTRODUCTION

The Ardnamurchan peninsula mainly consists of Tertiary igneous rocks intruded into Moine Schists and thin overlying Mesozoic sediments.

The igneous rocks here constitute a centre of Tertiary igneous activity, one of several such centres found on the western coast of Scotland, the others occurring in Skye, Rhum, Mull and Arran. These Tertiary igneous rocks (including Rockall, the Small Isles, Morvern, St Kilda and Ailsa Craig) form part of the North Atlantic or Thulean province which extends to N. Ireland, the Faroes, Iceland and Greenland. Recently, another such centre has been described in the Blackstones Bank off west Scotland (McQuillin *et al.* 1975), termed the Blackstones complex (Fig. 1).

Four main events are recognised in the development of most of the igneous complexes in the British Tertiary province. These are:

1. Eruption of basic lavas which are mainly alkali-olivine basalts. The thickness of these varies throughout the Scottish Tertiary Province, from 1500 m in Mull to 600 m in Skye, and approximately 100 m in Ardnamurchan, where some of the flows may have been removed by erosion.

2. Establishment of central vents giving rise to vent agglomerates and tuffs, with associated small flows of rhyolites, pitchstones and porphyritic basalt.

3. Emplacement of plutonic and hypabyssal rocks occurred at central complexes. The intrusive rocks are arcuate or annular in form and arranged concentrically round one or several centres (within a single igneous complex). Richey and others delineated three main centres of igneous activity in Ardnamurchan in their classic Memoir of 1930. The concentric intrusions consist of

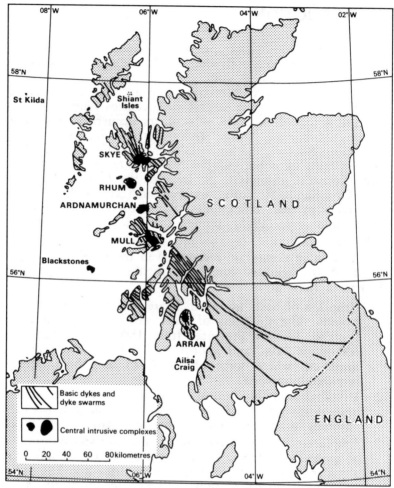

FIG. 1. The Tertiary igneous centres of Scotland and their associated dyke swarms (based on Richey *et al.* 1930).

thick ring dykes, up to 2 km thick. In Ardnamurchan most of these are composed of gabbro or dolerite, but range from eucrite types to monzonite and granophyre, with occasional composite (acid/basic) rock types. Most ring complexes are not circular in plan but more often oval in shape such as Centre 3 of Ardnamurchan which is roughly oval with a north-east to south-west long axis. The ring dykes are accompanied by cone-sheets, which are also arranged concentrically round the same centres of igneous activity. The cone-sheets are thin (less than 3 m thick) usually basic but can be composite with later acid granophyric or felsitic material intruded into the earlier basic magma. Cone-sheets are inclined inwards and downwards towards a common focus, at variable angles depending on their distance from this focus. In Ardnamurchan, Centre 2 possesses two sets of cone-sheets; an inner, steeply dipping set and an outer set, which dips at much shallower angles. If both sets are projected downwards with their observed angles of inclination, a depth for the focus of about 5 km is deduced; and other Hebridean suites of cone-sheets give similar results. These data fit quite well with modern estimates of subsurface geology (see section 4 below).

4. Intrusions of swarms of dykes (accompanied by sills) are taken as forming the final phase. This is an over-simplification for, although many dykes were intruded late in the sequences of events, the evidence from Mull and Skye suggests that igneous activity also began with dyke intrusion feeding the early plateau basalt lava flows and that dyke emplacement occurred at a number of stages throughout the development of these complexes.

Unlike the dykes associated with Skye, Mull and Arran, those of Ardnamurchan show no radial component in their distribution. This may imply that the Ardnamurchan centres are the surface expressions of a much smaller plutonic body than, for instance, Mull, which acted as a focus for dyke intrusion throughout its active history. The relative smallness of the body underlying the Ardnamurchan centres is confirmed by interpretation of the gravity anomalies over the Hebridean igneous complexes (Bott and Tuson 1973). These studies imply that Ardnamurchan is underlain by a vertical cylindrical body of gabbroic composition with a diameter of 12 km, extending to a depth of 4.5 km, compared with the Skye centre which has a diameter of 20 km and a depth extent of 16 km.

In Ardnamurchan, the igneous complexes consist of volcanic vents, ring intrusions and cone-sheets, which are concentrically arranged around three separate centres of intrusion.

Igneous activity began with the extrusion of basalt lavas and continued with the formation of small explosion vents which pierce both the basalts and the earlier country rocks (Moine schists and Mesozoic sediments). The vents are frequently infilled with agglomerates containing fragments of rocks which include some acid extrusive types, the original outcrops of which are no longer in existence. Associated with these early vents are small areas of extrusive and intrusive igneous activity, represented by pitchstone lavas and various porphyritic basic rocks. From the arrangement of these rocks and the large numbers of associated cone-sheets, an early centre of intrusion (or centre of igneous activity) called Centre 1 is recognised, which is situated in the eastern peninsula area (Fig. 2).

Another centre of intrusion (Centre 2) is similarly recognised, on the outcrop pattern of several ring dykes and two sets of cone-sheets, in the western peninsula area (Fig. 2).

Like Centre 1, most of Centre 2 has been replaced by igneous rock masses related to the youngest centre (Centre 3), located almost midway between the two earlier centres.

4

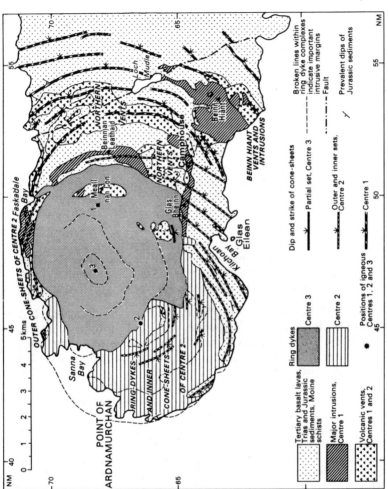

FIG. 2. The Tertiary intrusive complexes of Ardnamurchan—Centres 1, 2 and 3 (based on Richey et al. 1930).

5

Centre 3 consists almost entirely of ring dykes with very rare cone-sheets. It contains neither volcanic vents nor extrusive rocks.

According to Richey *et al.* (1961), the time sequence of events is as follows, beginning with the earliest events:

Centre 1   Volcanic vents mainly filled with agglomerates and traversed by cone-sheets and major intrusions often ambiguous in form.

Centre 2   Abundant outer cone-sheets surrounding later ring dykes essentially basic in composition. These ring dykes are divided into two age groups, respectively earlier and later than an inner set of cone-sheets. A volcanic vent associated with this centre (Glas Eilean) is later than the outer cone-sheets.

Centre 3   A suite of basic and ultrabasic ring dykes surrounds innermost acid igneous types (tonalite and quartz-monzonite). The outermost (and earliest) ring dyke is cut by some cone-sheets.

The cone-sheets are usually composed of dolerite, but occasionally may be composite with granophyric centres. The basic ring dykes consist of gabbroic rocks, sometimes displaying fluxion structures, and the ultrabasic rocks are invariably eucrite in type.

Evidence afforded by these plutonic intrusions for the presence of three distinct centres of intrusion is very limited. For instance, the attitude of the layering in the hypersthene-gabbro of Ardnamurchan Point (Centre 2) is ambiguous (Skelhorn and Elwell 1972), and the arcuate outcrops of the older gabbro of Lochan an Aodainn of Centre 2 may be controlled by younger intrusions. Even Richey *et al.* (1930) suggest that the Centre 2 gabbros of Beinn Bhuidhe and Portuairk may be related to Centre 3. Thus it is possible that the plutonic intrusions of Centres 2 and 3 may be continuous.

The age of the Tertiary igneous activity has been the subject of much discussion (see Table 1).

Area	Age (million years—m.y.)						
	62	60	58	56	54	52	50
Skye	L			PD	D		
Rhum			P				
Mull		L	P	D		D?	
Arran			P				
Ardnamurchan			PD				

L=lavas   P=plutonic intrusions   D=dykes

Table 1. Radiometric ages of Tertiary igneous rocks (based on Macintyre *et al.* 1975).

According to Table 1, the formation of the Tertiary igneous province commenced with a *major phase* of lava extrusion followed by emplacement of plutonic central complexes *c.* 59 m.y. ago (within the range 62 to 57 m.y.); and later by a *minor phase* of dyke intrusion *c.* 52 m.y. ago (within the range 56 to 52 m.y.).

Green and Wright (1969), assuming negligible differential movements, cannot envisage how an older land surface, such as the surface-deposited volcanics of Centre 1 on Ben Hiant, can be preserved at a lower topographical level than younger plutonic rocks, such as those of Beinn na Seilg (Centre 2) and Meall Meadhoin (Centre 1), which must have solidified beneath at least 1000 m of domed overburden. They suggest that the Ben Hiant event could be a flank eruption younger than both the Centre 2 and Centre 3 activity, implying that the cone-sheets of Centre 1 were also emplaced at a late stage in the evolution of the complex. Le Bas (1971) points out that differential movement must have taken place when the cone-sheets were emplaced, resulting in uplift of the central areas of the complex by an amount determined by the thickness and dip of the cone-sheets (Kuenen 1937), but Green and Wright (1974) note that the cone-sheets must also have produced a considerable increase in the topographic level of Ben Hiant. Isotopic age determinations on various Ardnamurchan rocks (Mitchell and Reen 1973) also appear to confirm the interpretation that the Ben Hiant event occurred at a late stage. A quartz-dolerite from the Ben Hiant intrusion gives an age of 55.9 ± 0.9 m.y. This is younger than the ages of both the Centre 1 cone-sheets (57.8 ± 0.9 m.y. to 61.4 ± 1.1 m.y.), and the Centre 2 cone-sheets (56.3 ± 1.2 m.y. to 60.7 ± 2.0 m.y.), but comparable with the age of the youngest plutonic intrusion of Centre 3 (56.4 ± 0.9 m.y. to 57.5 ± 0.8 m.y.).

Thus, if the relative age of the cone-sheets and related structures in the complex cannot be clearly determined, the separate identities of the three centres also becomes open to question. Nevertheless, as no clear reinterpretation of the position of the plutonic intrusions and cone-sheets of Ardnamurchan has yet emerged, the classification established by Richey *et al.* (1930) must still be regarded as the most reasonable, and is the one which has been used throughout this account.

THE MOINE COUNTRY ROCKS

The oldest rocks of the region are found to the east of the main Tertiary complex, and also along the southern part of the Ardnamurchan peninsula between Kilchoan Bay and Ben Hiant. These metamorphic rocks belong to the Precambrian Moine series. Radiometric dating on similar rocks to the east of this has confirmed this.

The rocks are psammitic in type comprising white or pale coloured, fairly pure sandstones, with occasional pelitic bands. In section the rocks consist of quartz and subordinate alkali-feldspar, with occasional iron ores and micas (both biotite and muscovite).

To the east of Ben Hiant, the Moine schists are isoclinally folded in tight vertical folds with north-west/south-east axes, but on the eastern flanks of Ben Hiant, and along the Kilchoan shore, the dips are shallow, usually less than 30° and to the west.

MESOZOIC SEDIMENTARY ROCKS

In Ardnamurchan, Mesozoic rocks outcrop in several areas, being best exposed along the southern shore, from Kilchoan Pier westwards for a distance of about 5 km. Smaller isolated exposures occur elsewhere, particularly between Sanna Point and Faskadale Bay, and also on the shore north of Swordle at Garbh Rudha. Richey *et al.* (1930) examined the sediments in detail, and reported that the rocks are Jurassic sediments with an occasional thin band of Trias sediments separating the Jurassic rocks from the underlying Moines. The succession and thicknesses of the modern stages and zones of the Jurassic found in Ardnamurchan are given in Table 2 with descriptions of each stratigraphic unit including some of the fossils obtained from each (Richey *et al.* 1930, ch. iv). The succession, which is given from youngest to oldest rocks, is not complete, only those zones actually found at Ardnamurchan being described.

JURASSIC (176m +)

Series (location and thickness)	Stages	Zones (recognised or equivalent strata)
Great Estuarine Series 3m (at Sron Bheag)	BATHONIAN and topmost BAJOCIAN	
	LOWER BAJOCIAN	Hyperlioceras discites subzone
Inferior Oolite (g^5) 35m in situ only at Maol Buidhe, 2km S.W. of Kilchoan	AALENIAN	Graphoceras concavum zone
		Ludwigia murchisonae zone
		Tmetoceras scissum zone
Upper Lias (g^3) 6m west shore of Kilchoan Bay 1.5km S.W. of Pier	TOARCIAN	Pleydellia aalensis subzone
		Dumortieria moorei subzone
Middle Lias (g^2) 12m north shore 3km east of Rudha Groulin	DOMERIAN	Scalpa Sandstone
On west side of Kilchoan Bay	LOWER PLIENSBACHIAN	Pabba Beds
Lower Lias (g^1) 120m + on foreshore, south of Mingary Pier	SINEMURIAN	—
	HETTANGIAN	Broadford Beds

TRIASSIC (<5m in thickness)

Found on foreshore at Kilchoan where Mingary pier is actually built on Trias. Also forms a thin band of sediments on eastern flank of Ben Hiant, separating the Tertiary rocks (basalts) from the underlying Moines

10 Table 2 Mesozoic rocks of Ardnamurchan.

black fissile shales with *Estheria murchisoniae*

blue shales or flags with *Docidoceras* and calcareous beds with *Reynesella:* also limestone with *Platygraphoceras*

hard white limestone with *Ludwigella cornu*

limestone with varied fauna including *Ludwigella flexilis,* blue sandy limestones and hard limestones with *Ludwigia* cf. *murchisonae*

limestone with doubtful *Ancolioceras (Hudlestonia sinon* subzone?)

sandy beds underlying limestones containing many species of *Leioceras*

dark flags and shales with *Pleydellia aalensis.*

flags and shales with cementstones containing *Dumortieria brancoi*

fine-grained purplish shales with limey ironstone (= **Raasay Ironstone**). Rocks frequently baked by Tertiary igneous intrusions, but have yielded various species of *Dactylioceras*

sandstone without fossils, often baked

sandy, well-bedded shales with poor fossiliferous horizons

including *Gryphaea obliquata* and other species of *Gryphaea,* belemnites and bivalves

hardened shales and thin limestones with *Ostrea* sp.

Various rock types comprise the **Trias** sediments, but generally these include red sandstones, conglomerates, schist-breccia and cornstones (fine-grained limestones). It should be noted that the basal Trias beds (conglomerates and red sandstones) are indistinguishable in the field from the Moines. No fossils have been discovered.

11

TERTIARY IGNEOUS ROCKS

BASALT LAVA FLOWS (alkali-olivine basalts)

These basalt lavas represent the earliest Tertiary igneous rocks, and occur in a broad north-south trending belt just east of Beinn an Leathaid, about 2 to 3 km wide at Faskadale in the north narrowing to about 1 km width at Camphouse in the south. Small outcrops of basalt are seen north and west of Glas Eilean on the Kilchoan foreshore, and to the west of Ben Hiant approximately 2 km east of Mingary, while other isolated basalt outcrops occur south of Aodann, on the southern side of Meall an Tarmachain and north of Meall nan Con. In all these places, the lavas occur in association with volcanic vent material. To the east of Ben Hiant, two outliers of basalt occur; one on the eastern flanks of Ben Hiant, and the other, larger one further to the east, separated from the first by a large north-north-west to south-south-east trending fault with a 75 m downthrow to the east. Loch Mudle is situated on this fault line and is probably fault controlled; the fault being called the Loch Mudle fault.

In the Ardnamurchan peninsula the total thickness of the lava flows is about 100 m. Individual flows frequently show signs of alteration and, as a result of subsequent vent explosions, are often brecciated. The greatest thickness of lava flows is seen in the wide belt trending southwards from Faskadale (in the Braehouse area), but since trap featuring is not present, details of the basalt structure and the total thickness of the lava pile are difficult to ascertain.

The lavas generally comprise plateau basalt (microporphyritic) types, but examples of macroporphyritic basalt and mugearite are seen in the Kilmory area, about 3 km east of Faskadale. The basalts are often vesicular with occasional amygdaloidal patches, and everywhere show extensive alteration. The small basalt outcrops in the west of the peninsula are often baked and thermally altered by later intrusions, and the later explosive vents have also disrupted the flows.

The freshest basalts are found in the eastern Ben Hiant area. Here they are black, microporphyritic (or non-porphyritic) with fine-grained ophitic texture. Phenocrysts of olivine with subordinate labradorite occur in a matrix of plagioclase feldspar, titaniferous augite, olivine and magnetite. Alkali-rich patches are found in which analcite and alkali-feldspar are present, together with augite often surrounded by a rim of aegirine. Patches of glass can also be recognised.

Some of the alteration may be caused by weathering, but much is caused by pneumatolytic action of later igneous intrusions.

The basalts commonly rest directly on the Moine schists, but in some areas thin beds of Jurassic sediments usually comprising mudstones, shales, sandstones and lime-stones intervene between the lavas and the basement Moines. On the eastern flanks of Ben Hiant the lavas rest on top of a basal Tertiary mudstone overlying Lower Lias limestones, which in turn rest on top of Triassic sandstones and grits.

CENTRE 1

The outcrop of the rocks which comprise Centre 1 is shown on Figure 2. They form a broad arcuate belt on the eastern part of Ardnamurchan from Faskadale Bay to Mingary Pier (approximately 3 km wide). Centre 1 mainly includes vent agglomerates, lavas and varied basic intrusive igneous rock types, and acid igneous rocks are rare.

Vent rocks (and associated extrusive rocks)

Richey *et al.* (1930) described these under two headings: the Ben Hiant vents and the Northern vents (Fig. 2). These

13

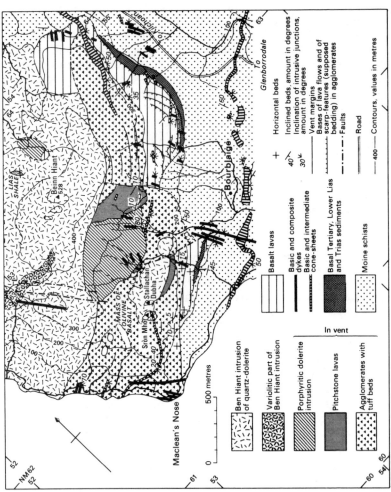

FIG. 3. The Ben Hiant vent-complex (based on Richey *et. al.* 1930 and Gribble 1974).

Legend:

Ben Hiant intrusion of quartz-dolerite

Variolitic part of Ben Hiant intrusion

In vent:
Porphyritic dolerite intrusion

Pitchstone lavas

Agglomerates with tuff beds

Basalt lavas

Basic and composite dykes

Basic and intermediate cone-sheets

Basal Tertiary, Lower Lias and Trias sediments

Moine schists

+ Horizontal beds

40 Inclined beds, amount in degrees

30 Inclination of intrusive junctions, amount in degrees

Vent margins

Bases of lava flows and of scarp-features (supposed bedding) in agglomerates

Faults

Road

400 Contours, values in metres

0   500 metres

14

vents constitute the first signs of igneous activity after the extrusion of plateau lava, and are fairly widespread in east Ardnamurchan, being found circling Ben Hiant (the Ben Hiant vents, Fig. 3) and also north of the Camphouse area, in an arcuate belt from Camphouse to Kilmory in the north at Faskadale Bay (the Northern vents). A few more isolated vents occur, particularly on the north-west shore at Rudha Carrach, inland at Meall nan Con and Meall an Tarmachain, and at Glas Eilean on the west side of Kilchoan Bay. Other vent rocks were ascribed to Centre 2 by Richey *et al.* (1930) and are described under the account of Centre 2 in this guide. However, their compositions are remarkably similar throughout Ardnamurchan.

The agglomerates consist of angular rock fragments of varying sizes as well as volcanic bombs, often of a very large size, held in a tuffaceous matrix. These fragments include rhyolite and dacite types, which are particularly well displayed in the Faskadale agglomerate. Trachytes and other intermediate volcanic types often showing vesicular textures also occur, but it is difficult to determine whether these rock fragments are bombs or disrupted blocks of lava. Fragments of some basaltic rocks have been observed in the agglomerates, particularly two huge masses of large-feldspar, porphyritic basalt near Maclean's Nose. In the Northern vents, large blocks of Mesozoic rocks have been observed, particularly near Achateny and Kilmory, and on the foreshore north of these settlements. Similar fragments have been observed within the other vents in the region.

The tuffaceous matrix is fine-grained with small grains of quartz and mica, probably derived from the early Moine country rocks, but the bulk of material constituting the tuffs is derived from igneous rocks, probably the earlier basalts.

The contact between the agglomerates and other rock types can be observed in several places, particularly in two vents which comprise the agglomerates on the east side of

Ben Hiant. In a stream on the east flank of Ben Hiant the agglomerate/basalt boundary of the northern vent is well displayed (dipping south-west at about 20°). This is much more gently inclined than that observed by Richey *et al.* (1930, p. 123) who consider 35° to 50° as the dip of the contact. However, observations in parallel stream valleys suggest that the dip of this contact is very variable.

Towards Maclean's Nose the junction between agglomerate and basalt, and agglomerate and Moine country rocks, of the southern Ben Hiant vent can be seen in several places on the scarp slope to the west of the abandoned village of Bourblaige. In this area, basalt blocks are found in the agglomerate more than one hundred metres below the present level of the *in situ* basalts, suggesting that the basalts must have fallen into the open vent at the time of its eruption. Very rarely is the contact between agglomerates and wall rocks (basalts or Moine country rocks) seen, but where observed, the contacts are steeply dipping and brecciation of the vent wall rock is often absent. This is in marked contrast to the Glas Eilean vent of Centre 2 on the shore east of Kilchoan Bay, where shattering of the wall rock is so marked that the boundary of this vent cannot be placed with any accuracy. In the broad belt of agglomerates trending north from Camphouse, comprising the Northern vents, the nature of the contact with country rocks is unknown, but north-west of Loch Mudle the agglomerate/Moine contact is very steep as seen in the valley of the Achateny Water.

In general, the agglomerates and tuffs found infilling the vents in Ardnamurchan represent the earliest eruptive phase, post-dating the extrusion of the plateau lavas. Evidence of pre-vent intrusions and igneous activity is provided by the fragments of acid igneous rocks (rhyolites and dacites etc.) found as fragments in the agglomerates, and also by a dyke cut by the agglomerate on the east side of Ben Hiant. In some cases evidence of violent formation is displayed by the highly brecciated margins (Glas Eilean), whereas in others (Maclean's Nose area) the wall rocks are smooth and show little brecciation.

Pitchstone lavas

Within the vents extrusive rocks occur, and the most important of these are the pitchstone lavas. These occur only on the south-east flank of Ben Hiant about 350 m above sea level, forming a knoll of rock rising above the lower escarpment (see Gribble 1970, pl. 1). The pitchstones are considered to be lava flows within the crater itself (i.e. the south Ben Hiant vent), and several flows are interbedded with tuffaceous material. Occasional columnar jointing is seen and the vesicular top of each flow is often infilled with minerals such as calcite and agate quartz. From the field evidence two or three flows are present.

The pitchstones are very fresh, extremely fine-grained, glassy rocks with small phenocrysts. Crystals of plagioclase feldspar and augite occur in a pale brown, glassy matrix containing some iron ores and apatite. The feldspars are labradorite with microliths of oligoclase set in the ground mass, and the augites are of a green aluminous variety, with rare crystals of orthopyroxene also present. The overall composition of the pitchstone lavas is similar to that of andesite.

The pitchstone lavas are thought to be contemporaneous with the initial phase of igenous activity, but to post-date the main plateau lavas.

Trachyte lavas

A small outcrop of trachyte material (possibly a plug) occurs to the east of Ben Hiant, within an area of Moine country rocks. The trachyte resembles blocks found within the vent agglomerates and may thus pre-date or be almost contemporaneous with the agglomerates and pitchstone lavas. This trachyte plug gives rise to a small crag near the

Kilchoan-Salen road, north of where the road crosses the Allt Tòrr na Mòine stream. The rock is a biotite-trachyte containing laths of alkali-feldspar in a felted arrangement, with plates of brown biotite, subordinate iron ores and augite.

Intrusive rocks (plutonic and hypabyssal types)

The remaining Centre 1 rocks are all intrusive igneous plutonic or hypabyssal types, usually basic, but with one acid intrusion of granophyre at Faskadale Bay. It is difficult to ascertain their order of age. Undoubtedly the agglomerates and lavas are the earliest but the sequence of the remaining intrusions is not known with certainty as most are rather isolated and quite small in size, apart from the dolerites of Ben Hiant and Beinn an Leathaid. These are described roughly in the order employed by Richey *et al.* (1930).

Gabbro of Meall nan Con

This small intrusion, which is now considered of doubtful age and is mentioned with Centre 3 rocks (p. 57) is intruded into plateau lavas and early agglomerates against which it shows a chilled margin, but is completely surrounded by the large ring dykes of Centre 3 which have thermally altered the rock.

The rock is a typical dark, olivine-bearing gabbro with basic plagioclase and augite found in an ophitic relationship, and with additional olivine and iron ores.

Quartz-gabbro of Faskadale

This is a dyke-like intrusion extending from west Faskadale Bay westwards for about 2 km. Although it appears to be continuous with an outer quartz-gabbro of Centre 3 (see p. 55), Richey *et al.* (1930, p. 145) assign it to Centre 1 because of the number of cone-sheets cutting it, which are older than Centre 3 rocks. It has suffered thermal alteration from the Centre 3 intrusions and the rock is highly sheared in places. Richey *et al.* (1930) consider that these factors make interpretation of this intrusion difficult and that probably more than one phase of emplacement exists.

Petrographically the intrusion is variable with typical quartz-gabbro and olivine-gabbro types present, the minerals being augite and plagioclase feldspars (labradorite in the olivine-bearing types, and more soda-rich feldspar in the quartz-bearing gabbros). Occasional veining of acidic granophyric material appears — a common occurrence in ring intrusions of Centres 2 and 3. Thermal alteration from Centre 3 intrusions has led to the development of green hornblende from olivine or olivine pseudomorphs. At Faskadale Bay the rock is more doleritic although frequent shear zones tend to obscure the mineralogy. The feldspars here are often highly altered, which may be due to the influence of the Faskadale granophyre which bounds it to the north, as well as the effects of shearing.

Granophyre of Faskadale

The granophyre post-dates the quartz-gabbro which forms a boundary to the south, as the granophyre is chilled against it. Some later basic cone-sheets cut the granophyre, which is acidic in composition and frequently contains xenoliths of schist. About 1 km west of Faskadale Bay, the granophyre is cut by a thin basic sheet of gabbroic texture. Westwards from this point the granophyre is more basic in composition.

The acidic granophyre has a micrographic texture in which minute alkali feldspar crystals are surrounded by a micrographic growth becoming coarser outwards.

The more basic granophyre has a similar texture, but contains acicular amphibole in addition to the quartz and feldspar of the acid variety. Some biotite and secondary chlorite patches also occur.

Some mineralogical changes are seen where the granophyre is in contact with the gabbroic sheet mentioned above (the granophyre becoming more basic with large amphibole crystals developing in the rock).

The dolerites

Three main dolerite intrusions are present (excluding the cone-sheets; see p. 48), of which the dolerites of Ben Hiant and Beinn an Leathaid are the largest and the most important.

However, a number of smaller intrusions also belong to Centre 1 and, although age relationships are difficult to ascertain, the earliest of these is the porphyritic dolerite.

Porphyritic dolerite

This comprises two masses, a small circular one south of Ben Hiant, and another more elongate east-west one approximately 4 km long, running from west of Glas Beinn to north of Camphouse.

The porphyritic dolerite of Ben Hiant appears as a dark, fine-grained dolerite with plentiful phenocrysts of plagioclase feldspar about 10 mm long. The intrusive nature of the dolerite is seen in a gully crossing its eastern margin, where the dolerite/agglomerate boundary dips north-west at 80°, the dolerite showing a chilled contact against the agglomerate.

The dolerite/pitchstone contacts suggest that the porphyritic dolerite was intruded during the infilling of the Ben Hiant vent.

In thin section the porphyritic dolerite exhibits labradorite phenocrysts in a fine-grained matrix of augite, acicular labradorite feldspar crystals and patches of brown glass containing microliths and iron ores. The phenocrysts show slight zoning and antiperthitic textures are common,

20

with a soda-rich feldspar phase exsolving. Various textures are formed within this intrusion; many of the most striking occurring along boundaries with other rock types (particularly the main Ben Hiant dolerite).

The other porphyritic dolerite running west and north from Camphouse exhibits similar mineralogy and textures, but is extremely badly exposed.

Quartz-dolerite of Camphouse

This intrusion mentioned by Richey *et al.* (1930, pp. 152-153) is now only exposed in an extremely weathered bank of rock on the stream behind the site of the old Camphouse farm. It is later than the porphyritic dolerites as it intrudes these.

Augite-diorite of Camphouse

This intrusion appears as a series of small knolls of rock about 1 km east-south-east of Camphouse farm, and the shape of the outcrop suggests a possible small circular intrusion with indeterminate age-relations with the other igneous rocks of Centre 1.

It is not indicated on the coloured map, but precise details of its location are given in the excursion description (6A). The hand specimen shows a very fresh, porphyritic, coarse-grained rock with large black augites more than 20 mm in length, contained in a white matrix of feldspar.

In thin section the augites exhibit zoning and are contained in a matrix of feldspar with accessory sphene and apatite. Two types of feldspar may be present — a labradorite and a perthitic potash feldspar both of which show extensive alteration.

The main dolerite intrusions of Beinn an Leathaid and Ben Hiant.

(a) The *Beinn an Leathaid dolerite* is a composite intrusion, which Richey *et al.* (1930) consider may represent a sheet-like body gently dipping to the west (Richey *et al.*, p. 156; *cf.* Gribble 1974, p. 76), comprising a doleritic base with a granophyric upper half, the total thickness being greater than 100 m.

On the ridge top, numerous xenoliths of schist and gneiss can be recognised within the granophyric upper part. The change from acid material to underlying dolerite occurs across a very narrow transition zone, well displayed on the cliffs east of the Beinn an Leathaid summit.

Petrographical investigation shows the dolerite to consist of labradorite feldspar (zoned with K-feldspar rims), augite and secondary amphibole set in a granophyric matrix comprising about 20% of the rock's volume. Magnetite also is present in reasonable amounts. The narrow transitional zone shows a decrease in the ferromagnesian minerals of the dolerite accompanied by a corresponding increase in the granophyric material, and the uppermost sheet of granophyre is rich in rock glass with occasional oligoclase and quartz.

(b) The *Ben Hiant dolerite* has recently been examined in detail by Gribble (1974). It forms the main summit of Ben Hiant having a thickness there of more than 200 m. Fresh dolerite is rare on the Ben Hiant crags which usually display excellent onion-skin weathering. The dolerites of Hiant were compared with the ring dyke dolerites of Centres 2 and 3 (Gribble 1974, p. 73), and the mineralogy given for both olivine-bearing and quartz-bearing dolerites as follows:

Olivine-dolerites	Quartz-dolerites
Plagioclase An_{63} (core) zoned to An_{30} (rim) Olivine Fa_{32} to Fa_{43}	Plagioclase An_{45} (core) zoned to An_{28} (rim)

Augite $Ca_{40}Mg_{34}Fe_{26}$ to $Ca_{33}Mg_{42}Fe_{25}$ (2V 38° to 52°)

The dolerites of Ben Hiant have variable modes, with plagioclase between 50% and 60%, augite 20%-30%, iron ore 3%-10%, and with olivine or quartz present depending upon the type of dolerite. Rare orthopyroxene may also occur.

All the dolerites of Centre 1 contain large amounts of glass, and although the main minerals of each rock type appear to have been in equilibrium with each other, the norms of all the dolerites except the most basic contain free quartz (Gribble 1974, table 3). These Ben Hiant dolerites are not found in the field in association with the variolite of Ben Hiant (Richey *et al.* 1930, p. 166), which probably represents early formed crystals and magmatic liquid which was quickly chilled during emplacement. It is unlikely that the dolerites of Ben Hiant represent a single large homogeneous intrusion. In large homogeneous intrusions regular changes in mineralogy and chemical composition occur within a differentiated sheet, numerous examples of which have been described. In a systematic sampling from top to bottom of Ben Hiant, there is not a simple progression from acidic material near the top to basic dolerite at the bottom; instead a series of steps occur of varying thicknesses and of different chemical compositions, which do not show regular changes. It is possible that the Ben Hiant dolerites represent several cone-sheets which have coalesced within the earlier volcanic vent (Gribble 1974); thus agreeing with the ideas of Geikie (1897). The variolite or glassy dolerites which occur in patches to the west-south-west of the Ben Hiant summit probably represent quickly chilled magma in which the normal doleritic minerals appear in a very fine-grained spherulitic texture. Analyses of dolerites of Ardnamurchan are plentiful (Richey *et al.* 1930; Skelhorn and Elwell 1966; Holland and Brown 1972; Gribble 1974), but no analyses of variolite exist, although the mineralogy of these rocks suggests that they will be similar to normal dolerites. Gribble (1974) also analysed the

C

rock glass contained in the normal dolerites, which proved to be very siliceous and Table 3 shows this, as well as including analyses of the main rock types from the Centre 1 dolerite.

	1	2	3	4	5	6
SiO_2	72.57	54.38	46.87	49.8	52.5	50.0
TiO_2	.32	2.29	2.33	1.0	1.0	2.5
Al_2O_3	10.54	13.51	13.45	13.9	13.5	13.0
Fe_2O_3	n.d.	4.72	4.83	9.7	—	—
FeO	5.90	7.96	10.71			
MnO	.10	.21	.23	—	—	—
MgO	.51	2.85	6.38	9.2	8.5	5.0
CaO	.47	6.37	8.62	12.9	12.0	10.0
Na_2O	3.22	3.13	2.38	1.8	2.0	2.8
K_2O	6.64	2.13	1.33	.2	1.0	1.2
P_2O_5	—	0.60	.38	—	—	—
H_2O	—	2.17	2.19	1.0	—	—
Total	100.27	100.32	99.70	99.5	100.00	97.5

Analyses from Gribble (1974, tables 1 and 5), except for no. 6.

1. Rock glass from dolerite on Ben Hiant.
2. Quartz-dolerite, Ben Hiant.
3. Olivine-dolerite, Ben Hiant.
4. Estimate of average primary cumulate of Centre 1.
5. Estimate of average primary magma of Centre 1.
6. Non-porphyritic central magma type (Bailey *et al.* 1924).

Table 3 Compositions of Centre 1 rocks and magmas.

The dolerites of Ben Hiant are therefore tholeiitic in composition, and show a light Fe-enrichment trend when plotted into an AFM diagram. Gribble (1974, p. 88) considers that the Centre 1 dolerites of Ben Hiant crystallised from a magma of approximately the composition of analysis no. 5 in the table above (roughly equivalent in composition to the non-porphyritic central magma type of Bailey *et al.* 1924, p. 14). The same magmatic source gave rise to the later dolerites of Centres 2 and 3 with slight elemental changes (richer in Al_2O_3 and Na_2O in 2 and 3, but poorer in SiO_2, Ba and Cu). Further studies by Gribble have suggested that the real differences may, in fact, lie between cone-sheets and ring dykes, with the cone-sheets of Centres 1 and 2 being from the same magmatic source (including the dolerites of Ben Hiant and Beinn an Leathaid). These cone-sheets perhaps post-date the basic ring dyke dolerites of Centres 2 and 3; which would explain why the magma giving rise to the cone-sheets is richer in SiO_2 and Ba (and probably Rb — though this is not easily detectable), and poorer in Al_2O_3 and Na_2O than the earlier basic magmas forming the ring dykes.

Since the cone-sheets of Centres 1 and 2 are essentially similar in composition and mineralogy, these are dealt with together at the end of the section on Centre 2.

CENTRE 2

Vent rocks

A small linear vent at Glas Eilean, south of Kilchoan, is generally considered to be related to Centre 2 (Richey *et al.* 1930; Paithankar 1967). It contains agglomerates with fragments of quartz-dolerite probably derived from the outer cone-sheets of Centre 2. However, these fragments are indistinguishable from the cone-sheets of Centre 1 and cannot provide evidence of the relative age of the vent. The vent is not cut by any of the Centre 2 cone-sheets.

Along the shore of Glas Eilean the vent is bounded by basalt lava to the north-west and Moine schists to the south and east (Fig. 4). The north-western margin is largely fault controlled. In addition to the quartz-dolerite, fragments of Moine schist, porphyritic basalt, Jurassic limestone, sandstone, and shale occur within a matrix which consists largely of devitrified glass. Details of the matrix show the

25

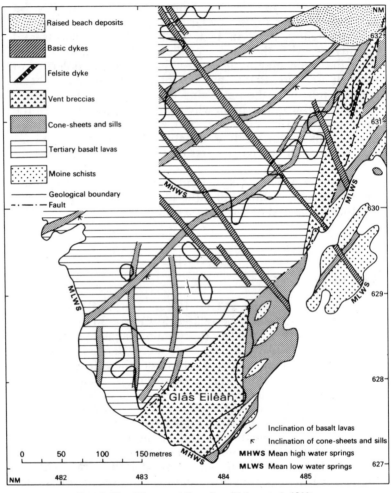

Raised beach deposits

Basic dykes

Felsite dyke

Vent breccias

Cone-sheets and sills

Tertiary basalt lavas

Moine schists

Geological boundary

Fault

Inclination of basalt lavas

Inclination of cone-sheets and sills

MHWS Mean high water springs

MLWS Mean low water springs

0 50 100 150 metres

Glas Eilean

FIG. 4. Glas Eilean vent (based on Richey *et al.* 1930).

26

presence of chloritic shards, suggesting a basic origin, and lenticular bodies consisting of chlorite spherulites together with quartz and alkali-feldspar spherulites. This indicates a unique association of acid and basic glass. Within the matrix are fragments up to 1 m long, usually angular, and thoroughly mixed, with some vertical displacement from their original positions.

Occupying an intricate veining system within the agglomerates is an acid tuff of devitrified acid glass enclosing bodies of basic devitrified glass. Occasionally acid nuclei occur within these basic bodies. A small acid dyke is also present cutting the agglomerate and showing fluxion structure parallel to its margins, which are also roughly parallel to the trend of the vent. Paithankar (1967) notes that the opposite walls of this dyke cannot be matched and, as it contains a large number of agglomerate fragments, suggests a non-dilatational mechanism of emplacement. The dyke rock is essentially rhyolitic in composition with quartz and feldspar phenocrysts, but texturally is similar to the matrix of the agglomerate and the vein material. Reynolds (1954) calls this rock an "intrusive ignimbrite", but Paithankar (1967) prefers the term tuffisite.

Paithankar (1967) considers that the vent was initiated by a shattering of the country rocks by gases, followed by gas-streaming which brought about the emplacement of the tuffisite. The intimate association of acid and basic glass provides evidence for liquid immiscibility in conditions of high water vapour pressure and super-heating.

Intrusive plutonic rocks

The sequence of intrusion of the plutonic rocks of Centre 2, described by Richey et al. (1930) is (from oldest to youngest):

	Hypersthene-gabbro of Ardnamurchan Point
Earlier than the inner cone-sheets	*Older gabbro of Lochan an Aodainn*
	Quartz-gabbro of Garbh-dhail
	Granophyre of Grigadale
	Older quartz-gabbro of Beinn Bhuidhe
	Quartz-gabbro of Aodann
	Granophyric quartz-dolerite of Sgùrr nam Meann
Later than the inner cone-sheets	*Eucrite of Beinn nan Ord*
	Quartz-gabbros of Loch Caorach and Beinn na Seilg
	Younger quartz-gabbro of Beinn Bhuidhe
	Fluxion gabbro of Portuairk
	Aodann felsite

Paithankar (1968) has cast doubt upon some of the relationships of the Grigadale granophyre and associated gabbros, while Richey (1933) reiterates an earlier suggestion that the younger quartz-gabbro of Beinn Bhuidhe is a westward continuation of the Centre 3 quartz-gabbro of Faskadale. The mechanism of ring dyke emplacement, involving the formation of a ring fault and subsidence above a magma chamber as a consequence of a wholesale reduction in magmatic pressure, as originally proposed by Bailey and Maufe (1916) and elaborated by Anderson (1936), is still largely accepted.

Hypersthene-gabbro of Ardnamurchan Point

This is the earliest of the ring-shaped intrusions of Centre 2, and is considered by Richey *et al.* (1930) to be a ring dyke, although its inner margin is everywhere in contact with younger intrusions. Wells (1954a) however, suggests that the intrusion probably extended as a continuous roughly circular mass before the inner part was displaced by later intrusions. The outer margin of the hypersthene-gabbro is bounded by Mesozoic sediments, Tertiary basalts, plutonic intrusions of Centre 1, and the outer cone-sheets of Centre 2. The Mesozoic rocks are folded into a dome which partly surrounds the hypersthene-gabbro, and this pre-dates the emplacement of the outer cone-sheets. Nevertheless, the formation of this dome, the emplacement of the cone-sheets and the intrusion of the hypersthene-gabbro, are events all probably closely related in time, especially as some cone-sheets post-date the hypersthene-gabbro. Moreover, the intrusion of the hypersthene-gabbro does not appear to have altered the inclination of the earlier cone-sheets.

Wells (1954a) recognises several different types of contact between the hypersthene-gabbro and the host rock. These are either simple contacts which may be flat-lying or dip outwards at various angles, or complex contacts where the form of the intrusion has been controlled by the structure of the adjacent host rock and stoping of blocks occurs; but these seem restricted to those few areas where the dip of the host rock is toward the intrusion. Numerous basic xenoliths occur within the hypersthene-gabbro, sometimes attaining the form of substantial inclined sheets which dip toward the centre of the mass. These inclusions cannot have been moved far from their place of origin, and their presence probably marks the vicinity of the roof or wall of the intrusion. From this evidence it can be argued that the hypersthene-gabbro now exposed is the upper part of a boss-like or cone-shaped intrusion immediately below an eroded roof. Wells (1954a) believes it to be probably cone-shaped, but Skelhorn and Elwell (1971) consider that the attitude of the contact at the present level of erosion is not consistent with this interpretation, and suggest a boss-like form with the hypersthene-gabbro occupying the space above a more or less cylindrical block which dropped as a result of cauldron subsidence.

Richey *et al.* (1930) recognise that the hypersthene-gabbro has a marginal facies of quartz-dolerite and quartz-gabbro, and Wells (1954a) notes that although the hypersthene-gabbro forms a distinct unit, it contains several different rock types which are often sharply bounded against their neighbours. A relatively fine-grained hypersthene-gabbro forms the predominant rock type, with a plagioclase grain size of 1-2 mm and ophitic pyroxene up to 20 mm across. The average modal composition is plagioclase 60%, pyroxene 30% (generally more than 20% augite and less than 10% hypersthene), olivine 8%, and iron ore about 2%. The hypersthene characteristically forms a discontinuous rim around olivine which continues outwards into sub-ophitic growths with plagioclase. In the absence of hypersthene, augite may partially enclose olivine, but when both pyroxenes are present, the augite forms independent ophitic growths.

Troctolitic gabbro, usually allivalitic in character, also occurs, but is a very subordinate rock type, giving rise to narrow bands which grade into peridotite. Coarser-grained, augite-rich xenolithic gabbros are found scattered throughout the intrusion. These tend to be more feldspathic than the hypersthene-gabbro, and also richer in iron ore. Gabbro pegmatites are rare in the hypersthene-gabbro, but are sometimes found near its outer margin. These pegmatites often possess cores of quartz-feldspar rock with granophyric texture, and may be produced by melting of inclusions, but they could be the result of liquid segregation.

As noted above, quartz-gabbro and quartz-dolerite occur as a marginal development. The width of the zone is usually less than 100 m, but these rocks grade into the hypersthene-gabbro and the position of the boundary is indeterminable. Skelhorn and Elwell (1971) believe this margin represents a chilled phase of the magma which produced the more central lithologies, but Richey *et al.*

(1930), Wells (1954a), and Richey and Harry (1963) consider that the intrusion as a whole involved two magmatic pulses, the early phase forming the marginal facies. Quartz-feldspar veins are a conspicuous feature of the marginal facies, being very abundant near the contact. The larger veins are highly feldspathic, but the smaller may be composed entirely of quartz.

One of the most interesting features of the hypersthene-gabbro is the presence of mineralogical layering. Richey *et al.* (1930) consider this to be a fluxion structure confined to a zone near the inner margin of the intrusion, but Wells (1954a) shows that the layering is more widespread. However, the layering is best and most extensively developed in the inner part of the outcrop, and even here it is confined to certain zones, which do not persist far either vertically or laterally (Figs. 5 and 6). Wells (1954a) lists the following essential features of the layering:

(a) The layers consist of variable proportions of olivine, augite, hypersthene, magnetite and plagioclase. Occasional bands of peridotite, anorthosite and thin seams of iron ore occur.

(b) Modal differences are accompanied by slight textural variations.

(c) The sequence of layers appears to be haphazard in most areas, although some degree of order is provided by occasional rhythmic banding between more feldspathic and more pyroxene-rich layers.

(d) Evidence of gravity stratification is provided by concentrations of pyroxene and iron ore toward the base of the layers, and eroded olivines.

(e) Thicknesses vary, even in adjacent layers, from about 10 mm to 1 m. Between layers, large thicknesses may show no banding.

(f) Layer surfaces dip inwards, steepening from about 10° where present near the outer margin, to about 60° near the inner margin.

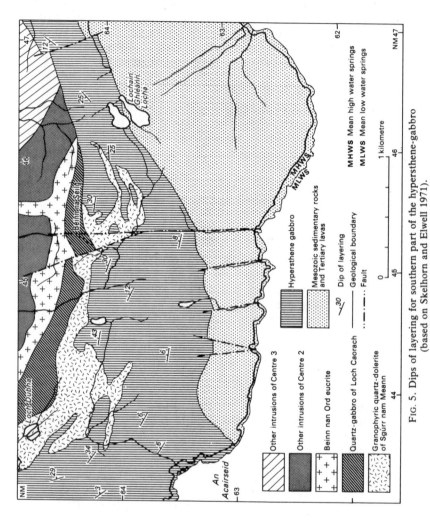

Fig. 5. Dips of layering for southern part of the hypersthene-gabbro (based on Skelhorn and Elwell 1971).

Other intrusions of Centre 3

Other intrusions of Centre 2

Beinn nan Ord eucrite

Quartz-gabbro of Loch Caorach

Granophyric quartz-dolerite of Sgùrr nam Meann

Hypersthene gabbro

Mesozoic sedimentary rocks and Tertiary lavas

30 Dip of layering

——— Geological boundary

·—·—· Fault

MHWS Mean high water springs

MLWS Mean low water springs

0   1 kilometre

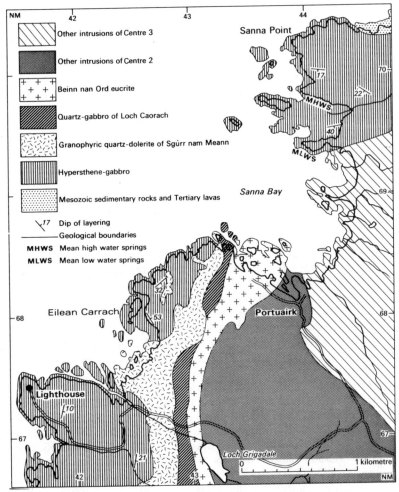

FIG. 6. Dips of layering for north-western part of the hypersthene-gabbro
(based on Skelhorn and Elwell 1971).

(g) Contacts between layers are generally sharp, but unchilled and with interlocking crystals.

(h) A crystallographic preferred orientation occurs parallel to the layering.

The under-surfaces of certain layers have protuberances similar in appearance to load-casts in sedimentary rocks. In a few places slumps occur, and occasionally erosion surfaces within the layers are observed. Skelhorn and Elwell (1971) consider that there is convincing evidence that the layering was produced by bottom accumulation on successive floors of a magma chamber, which were more or less horizontal. However, as the dip of the layering steepens inwards, they suggest that a phase of later deformation must have occurred, letting down as much as 75% of the intrusion along a central ring-fault, and downwarping the layering in the adjacent rock. The formation of this ring-fault permitted the emplacement of the granophyric quartz-dolerite of Sgùrr nam Meann which, in turn, obliterated direct evidence for the presence of the fault. Palaeomagnetic studies by Wells and McRae (1969) show that this process must have occurred before the layered rocks had cooled below their Curie temperature of about 570°C.

Sedimentary xenoliths have been recognised in the gabbro (Wells 1951), and in addition Wells (1954a) recognises inclusions of igneous origin which may have been formed by three main processes. Firstly, he believes that the presence of primary basalt and dolerite can be recognised by a relict porphyritic structure, while the presence of recrystallised amygdales allows the separate recognition of basalt. Secondly, autometamorphism of an early chilled facies of the gabbro itself may result in inclusions. Richey et al. (1930) regard this as a widespread phenomenon, but Wells (1954a) considers this difficult to prove. Finally, the hypersthene-gabbro may have incorporated narrow dyke-like bodies, producing a marginal interlamination between the dykes and the gabbro. These interlamination structures

34

suggest that shearing took place on opposite sides of the dyke during its injection and consolidation. The dykes also show a fluxion structure, and as no chilling effects are exhibited, the hypersthene-gabbro was probably still hot when the dyke material was crystallising. The dykes may have been derived either from pockets of magma lying within the crystallising hypersthene-gabbro, or from the partial fusion and mobilisation of xenolithic material.

Some of the most interesting xenolithic masses are the sapphire-bearing rocks which occur on the northern slope of Glebe Hill, north of Kilchoan village near the Amhainn Chrò Bheinn stream, where the hypersthene-gabbro is in contact with basaltic lava. The intrusion here may be an early consolidation phase which contains xenoliths of aluminous country rock, such as an aluminous bole produced by the weathering of the adjacent Tertiary lava, in which thermal alteration allowed the growth of sapphire. Alternatively, the sapphire may have formed in xenoliths which were only moderately aluminous, additional alumina having been added from the magma. Previous to Wells' (1951) work, these provided the only examples of xenoliths for which a sedimentary origin had been proposed, a remarkable fact since sedimentary rocks form the principal host for the intrusion. Even the sedimentary inclusions recognised by Wells (1951) are of very minor quantitative importance. Some rounded blocks of sandstone, now in the form of aegirine-granophyre cores surrounded by pyroxenite, occur near Rubha Carrach, and finely laminated blocks are found near Sanna Point. These latter inclusions consist of basic andesine surrounded by hypersthene, and with an outer zone of norite, in which layers of hypersthene and magnetite suggest relict bedding. The magnetite may represent ironstone bands.

Wells (1951) considers that the "basic granular hornfels" xenoliths are probably of sedimentary origin but Brown (1954) considers that to derive these from sedimentary rocks would require much metasomatic replacement, as well as complete recrystallisation. Instead he suggests that these are thermally metamorphosed layered ultrabasic or basic igneous rocks, derived from some level beneath the layered hypersthene-gabbro.

Older gabbro of Lochan an Aodainn

This is the only intrusion of Centre 2 which possesses a volcanic host on parts of its inner margin. Where these agglomerates and basaltic lavas, which are similar to those associated with Centre 1 activity, are present, the gabbro becomes fine-grained and resembles a quartz-dolerite. The remainder of its contacts are formed by younger intrusions, so that no original marginal modifications are apparent. Richey *et al.* (1930) consider that sufficient of the original inner wall is preserved to demonstrate a curvature about the focus of Centre 2 at Aodann (the old settlement centred round the Sonachan Hotel), and that the gabbro is in the form of a ring dyke and does not merely form a capping to the later quartz-gabbros with which it is in contact. However, if the volcanics are viewed as the remains of a once, more extensive screen, the use of their contact with the gabbro as an indicator of the focus of Centre 2 becomes very uncertain.

Although definite age relationships cannot easily be determined, the gabbro is certainly early. Even though it is traversed by only a single cone-sheet, it is definitely older than both the quartz-gabbro of Garbh-dhail and the Grigadale granophyre, both of which are extensively intruded by the inner cone-sheet suite of Centre 2.

The rock was originally an olivine-bearing dolerite but is now highly altered. Alteration effects are principally a marked cloudiness to the feldspars, and physical crushing and shattering, accompanied by a segregation and migration of acid material which locally assumes the character of an augite-granophyre. Occasionally masses of fine-grained basic rock occur within the gabbro.

Quartz-gabbro of Garbh-dhail

The arc formed by the outcrop of this intrusion is very restricted, being limited to the north by the Grigadale granophyre, and to the east by the quartz-gabbro of Faskadale (Centre 3). Great variations in both composition and texture occur throughout the mass, with the quartz-gabbro in several places grading into a quartz-dolerite with porphyritic feldspar. The modal composition of this rock, as xenoliths within the Grigadale granophyre, is: quartz 9.4%, plagioclase (zoned) 61.2%, pyroxene 20.1%, iron ore 5% and apatite 4.3%. A sharp, intrusive contact between different varieties of quartz-gabbro has been observed, indicating perhaps a composite intrusion. Indeed, Paithankar (1968) considers that whereas some parts of the intrusion are clearly older than the adjacent Grigadale granophyre, others are younger.

Xenoliths are locally abundant, and sometimes occur as bands of fine-grained basic rock similar to the xenoliths in the hypersthene-gabbro of Ardnamurchan Point (p. 29). Acid veins generally traverse the quartz-gabbro and the xenolithic bands. Both the quartz-gabbro and the acid veins are cut by the inner cone-sheet suite of Centre 2. The quartz-gabbro is clearly younger than the hypersthene-gabbro with which it makes contact at Beinn na Seilg, but older than the eucrite of Beinn nan Ord. Its inner margin shows chilling against the gabbro of Lochan an Aodainn, with the development of a fine-grained quartz-dolerite marginal facies.

Granophyre of Grigadale

As the largest mass of granitic rock in Ardnamurchan this intrusion deserves special attention. It is in contact with the gabbro of Lochan an Aodainn, the quartz-gabbro of Garbh-dhail, and both the younger and older quartz-

37

gabbros of Beinn Bhuidhe. Richey *et al.* (1930) consider the granophyre to be younger than the Garbh-dhail and Lochan an Aodainn gabbros, but older than both the Beinn Bhuidhe gabbros. Paithankar (1968), however, produces evidence that it includes xenoliths of the older gabbro of Beinn Bhuidhe. He also observes that whereas in some places the quartz-gabbro of Garbh-dhail is chilled against the granophyre, in others the reverse is the case. The granophyre is typically fine-grained, medium grey in colour with dark spots of altered augite and magnetite. Its modal composition is: quartz 4.5%, plagioclase (zoned, and edged with orthoclase) 60.8%, acid mesostasis (micrographic matrix of quartz and alkali-feldspar) 26.3%, augite 2.7% and iron ore 5.7%. Richey *et al.* (1930) consider the whole granophyre to be contaminated with gabbroic material. Paithankar (1968) believes that emplacement of the granophyre was accomplished by a fluidised system, initiated by a ring-fault, in which a gas-liquid-solid emulsion produced shattering of the solid gabbros and their incorporation into the granophyre.

Older quartz-gabbro of Beinn Bhuidhe

This small intrusion lies to the south of the younger quartz-gabbro of Beinn Bhuidhe and to the north of the Grigadale granophyre. Richey *et al.* (1930) believe it to be clearly younger than the granophyre, with the development of a chilled margin, but Paithankar (1968) reverses this sequence, and suggests a correlation with the older phase of the quartz-gabbro of Garbh-dhail. However, its invasion by the inner cone-sheet suite of Centre 2 shows it to be earlier than the younger quartz-gabbro of Beinn Bhuidhe, which is unaffected by these cone-sheets. It is a medium-grained rock with veins and patches throughout of acid material. A typical modal composition is: plagioclase 47%, acid mesostasis 23.3%, quartz 2.4%, pyroxene 19.1% and iron ore 8.2%.

Quartz-gabbro of Aodann

This intrusion forms the central zone of the Centre 2 complex, and is cut by the inner suite of cone-sheets. Its outer margin occupies an irregular arc of about 180° with the older gabbro of Lochan an Aodainn, against which it grades rapidly into a quartz-dolerite with porphyritic feldspar. Apart from this marginal modification, the quartz-gabbro also shows considerable variation both in texture and the development of an acid mesostasis. This variation leads to the recognition of two main types, a fine-grained gabbro with porphyritic feldspar, and a coarser grained non-porphyritic gabbro. Both sharp and gradational contacts between these two types are present, and where sharp contacts occur the fine-grained rock usually shows thermal alteration. Furthermore, the two varieties differ in their marginal behaviour against the Lochan an Aodainn gabbro, the finer rock having sharply defined chilled contacts, while the coarser rock becomes hybridized near the contact. Richey *et al.* (1930) consider that this evidence indicates two phases of injection, the finer grained rock forming first as a capping to the succeeding intrusion of coarser gabbro.

Near the junction with the Great Eucrite of Centre 3, the gabbro is finer grained and more basic in composition than elsewhere, while near the contact with the felsite south of Aodann, a porphyritic texture is developed. No contact is visible with the younger gabbro of Beinn Bhuidhe, which lies north-west of Aodann. Paithankar (1968) suggests a correlation with the older phase of the quartz-gabbro of Garbh-dhail.

Granophyric quartz-dolerite of Sgùrr nam Meann

Three rock types present within this intrusion include porphyritic dolerite (with feldspar phenocrysts), aphyric dolerite and granophyre (Fig. 7). The granophyre is developed as net-veins in the dolerites and locally in the

D

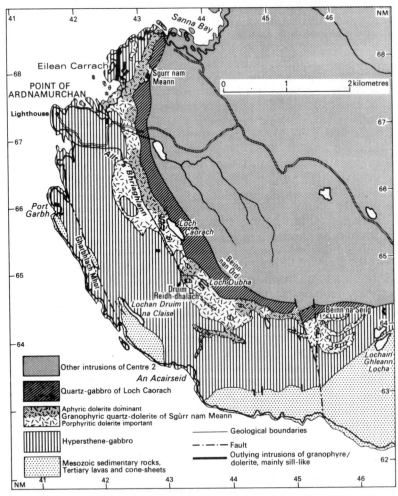

41   42   43   Sanna Bay 44   45   46   NM

Eilean Carrach

68

POINT OF
ARDNAMURCHAN

Sgùrr nam
Meann

Lighthouse

0   1   2 kilometres

67

Allt Bhriaghlann

Port
Garbh

66

Loch
Caorach

Gharbhlach Mhor

Beinn
nan Ord

65

Druim
Reidh-dhalach

Loch Dubha

Lochan Druim
na Claise

Beinn na Seilg

Lochain
Ghleann
Locha

64

Other intrusions of Centre 2

An Acairseid

Quartz-gabbro of Loch Caorach

Aphyric dolerite dominant
Granophyric quartz-dolerite of Sgùrr nam Meann
Porphyritic dolerite important

Hypersthene-gabbro

Mesozoic sedimentary rocks,
Tertiary lavas and cone-sheets

Geological boundaries

Fault

Outlying intrusions of granophyre/
dolerite, mainly sill-like

63

62

FIG. 7. The granophyric quartz-dolerite and associated intrusions of Centre 2
(based on Skelhorn and Elwell 1971).

adjacent hypersthene-gabbro of Ardnamurchan Point. The inner margin is determined by the later intrusion of the quartz-gabbro of Loch Caorach, which has in some places fused the acid component of the granophyric quartz-dolerite, and this fused material has back-veined the quartz-gabbro, causing the development of a gradational contact. The outer contact is formed by the hypersthene-gabbro. On Beinn na Seilg the contact is flat-lying, the hypersthene-gabbro clearly forming a capping to the granophyric quartz-dolerite. Immediately to the south of Beinn na Seilg, however, the contact dips south at about 30°. Still further south, northerly dipping contacts are present. Skelhorn and Elwell (1966) suggest that detailed variation in the form of the contact is controlled by the attitude of the layering in the hypersthene-gabbro, marginal sills having formed parallel to the layering. The general dip of the contact is, nevertheless, outwards at between 25° and 30°, although a few areas do occur where steeper dips are found. The intrusion as a whole does not, therefore, have the form of a ring dyke at the present level of erosion. Indeed, the development of sheeted relationships suggests that magmatic emplacement was not vertical for parts of the intrusion. Skelhorn and Elwell (1966) list four possible forms of the intrusion; namely a ring dyke in which contacts are stepped, the present erosion level coinciding with a shallow step; a sill which connected centrally with a ring dyke or plug now replaced by later intrusions; a marginal remnant of ring dyke cap; or lastly, a ring dyke with a number of sills given off outwards (as proposed by Wells 1954b). This last possibility is probably the most reasonable, as Butchins (1973) records the presence of several sheets of granophyric dolerite cutting the hypersthene-gabbro between Sanna Bay and Sanna Point. Similarly, in the area of Plocaig, the sheet of granophyre (considered to be an acid cone-sheet by Richey *et al.* 1930) which cuts the hypersthene-gabbro is probably an extension of the granophyric quartz-dolerite.

The association of the granophyre with the aphyric dolerite is most interesting. The granophyre may contain inclusions of dolerite up to 10 m or more across, many of the large inclusions being rounded. In some places the dolerite inclusions have a fine-grained margin against the granophyre, ranging from a few centimetres to a metre wide. In other places nearby, or even on a different section of the same contact where the dolerite may have an angular contact with the granophyre, the dolerite can possess uniform texture throughout. Inclusions with a fine-grained margin often contain a faint banding parallel to their contact with the granophyre, and in some there occurs a development of minute feldspathic veins also parallel to the contact.

Net-veins of granophyre are given off sporadically into the wall rocks or dolerite bodies. The material of these net-veins appears to fill fractures in the dolerite, as dolerite blocks are often of such shape that they would approximately fit together were the veining material removed. Toward the large scale veins from which they arise, the net-veins may widen and include disorientated fragments of dolerite which cannot be so reconstructed. Skelhorn and Elwell (1966) believe that the small, entirely fine-grained bodies, and those larger bodies with fine-grained margins, formed by being enclosed in a granophyric magma when still unconsolidated. The angular bodies which do not show a fine-grained margin, and those with net-veining, must have formed after the dolerite had solidified.

The granophyric veining in the porphyritic dolerite is in the form of irregular sill-like and dyke-like bodies. Although the porphyritic dolerite only forms angular masses, both fine-grained margins coarsening inwards and coarse textures throughout are found. These are thought to have been formed in the same manner as the features seen in the aphyric dolerite. Detailed relationships between porphyritic dolerite, aphyric dolerite and granophyre, show that the emplacement of the porphyritic dolerite preceded that of the aphyric dolerite, a sequence confirmed by the presence of fragments of porphyritic dolerite within the aphyric dolerite. The intrusion is cut by members of the inner cone-sheet suite of Centre 2. Gribble (1974), in a geochemical study, compares the composition of the aphyric dolerite with dolerites associated with Centre 1 cone-sheets (the main Ben Hiant dolerite intrusion) and Centre 3 ring dykes, and finds little chemical difference with the rocks from Centre 3, but significant difference with those from Centre 1. This may indicate that whereas the petrogenesis of the cone-sheet dolerites is distinct from that of the ring dyke dolerites, there is no such distinction between ring dykes from Centres 2 and 3.

Eucrite of Beinn nan Ord

Resistance to weathering results in this intrusion generally forming higher ground than the quartz-gabbros on either flank. Its dyke-like form is better displayed than any other ring dyke in Ardnamurchan, with steeply dipping contacts apparent on Beinn na Seilg and Beinn nan Ord. This ring dyke is also characterised by the presence of two inwardly projecting arms, which cut through the earlier quartz-gabbro of Garbh-dhail. Further evidence for the relative age of this intrusion is provided by the absence of cone-sheets in the eucrite, whereas cone-sheets can be seen in the quartz-gabbro of Garbh-dhail to within a short distance of its margin with the eucrite. Brecciation makes the exact position of the contact difficult to discover, but nearby the eucrite generally becomes finer grained, and shows fluxion structure, while the quartz-gabbro becomes thermally altered.

The eucrite is a moderately coarse-grained rock composed of fairly abundant olivine, ophitic greenish-brown augite with associated iron ores, and a basic plagioclase of the labradorite-bytownite type which frequently shows extensive albitization. In some parts the intrusion is allivalitic, while in others the rock is rich in clinopyroxene. Intermixture of these two types can also be seen. Small rounded masses of coarsely ophitic, augite-rich eucrite, which occur in the more allivalitic parts, are suggested by Richey et al. (1930) to be cognate xenoliths. In many places the rock shows the effects both of brecciation and the later emplacement of granophyric material, which also forms patches of quartz and orthoclase. Richey et al. (1930) believe that after emplacement the eucrite was subjected to explosive shattering by an acid magma.

Quartz-gabbros of Loch Caorach and Beinn na Seilg

Although forming separate intrusions, these two masses are considered by Richey et al. (1930) to be portions of a single ring dyke, but they differ in rock type, the quartz-gabbro of Beinn na Seilg being distinguished by the presence of a secondary acid mesostasis, and so the correlation is not immediately obvious. The outer contact of both intrusions is generally against the granophyric quartz-dolerite, and inclusions, sometimes very large, of this rock are found in the marginal parts of the quartz-gabbros. Marginal areas also usually show the development of thin acid veins. On Beinn na Seilg, part of the outer contact of the quartz-gabbro is with the hypersthene-gabbro of Ardnamurchan Point. Members of the inner cone-sheet suite of Centre 2, which cut the granophyric quartz-dolerite and hypersthene-gabbro, do not penetrate the quartz-gabbro, but show evidence of thermal alteration in its vicinity. The inner contact of both gabbros is with the eucrite of Beinn nan Ord. In detail this is obscured by brecciation that affects not only the eucrite but the adjoining portion of the quartz-gabbros. North of Loch Caorach a sharp contact is seen, with the quartz-gabbro becoming finer toward the eucrite, but on the southern shore of Sanna Bay the contact is very vague. Richey et al. (1930) suggest these features indicate that there is little difference in age between the eucrite and quartz-gabbros, and one injection followed closely upon the other.

These gabbros, like many other gabbros in Ardnamurchan, show considerable variation in the amount of late crystallising acid material and the effects of this on the earlier formed constituents. In its least modified from, the magma has crystallised as an olivine-gabbro of eucritic affinities, but the olivine is usually decomposed. On Beinn na Seilg the intrusion has been affected by the migration of an acid magma, causing either hybridization or the development of an acid mesostasis. The effects of this later acid migration had been much less intense on the intrusion of Loch Caorach resulting only in a general albitization of the feldspars in the rock.

Younger quartz-gabbro of Beinn Bhuidhe

Unlike the older quartz-gabbro of Beinn Bhuidhe, this intrusion is not cut by the inner cone-sheets of Centre 2. Both the older quartz-gabbro and the cone-sheets show thermal alteration near their contact with this later intrusion, while the older quartz-gabbro is also intruded by quartz-dolerite which connects with the younger quartz-gabbro of Beinn Bhuidhe. The intrusion of the younger quartz-gabbro is also clearly a later event than the emplacement of the Beinn nan Ord eucrite, a screen of thermally altered eucrite occurring with a steeply dipping contact within the quartz-gabbro near the northern summit of Beinn Bhuidhe. There also, a coarse-grained, light weathering quartz-gabbro in contact with the fluxioned margin of a dark weathering quartz-gabbro suggests that the mass may include more than one intrusion. Elsewhere the rock is highly variable, with the development of an acid mesostasis. Near the contact with the Great Eucrite of Centre 3, the rock becomes fine-grained, and has been largely recrystallised. No contacts are visible with the fluxion gabbro of Portuairk or the quartz-gabbro of Aodann. Richey *et al.* (1930), and Richey

(1933), have suggested that this intrusion is probably a westward continuation of the quartz-gabbro of Faskadale, which will be considered in the section on the plutonic rocks of Centre 3.

Fluxion gabbro of Portuairk

Although mapped as a distinct unit by Richey *et al.* (1930), because of the widespread development of a characteristic fluxion structure, this mass is clearly of a mixed nature, and has been produced by the modification of gabbroic or eucritic material by an acid magma. This interaction may have taken place with the basic rock in a solid or partially solid condition, but before the intrusion of the mass into its present position. The migration of an even later phase of acid magma has locally exaggerated the effects of this alteration.

The contacts of the mass with the three adjacent intrusions are generally obscure. Although an apparent contact with the Great Eucrite of Centre 3 is seen on the coast, in which the fluxion gabbro would appear the earlier intrusion, there is no marked contact alteration, and the exact significance of this contact is complicated by the fact that the outer part of the Great Eucrite is itself a fluxion rock.

Richey *et al.* (1930) suggest that the mass is later than the younger quartz-gabbro of Beinn Bhuidhe. If their correlation of that intrusion with the quartz-gabbro of Faskadale is accepted, it follows that the formation of the fluxion gabbro of Portuairk is more properly considered a Centre 3 event. They suggest its likely correlation with the fluxion gabbro of Faskadale. A detailed account of fluxion structures in gabbros is given on p. 63.

Aodann felsite

Small masses of dark grey, microporphyritic felsite are found cutting various members of the plutonic suite and the

46

inner cone-sheets of Centre 2. The largest intrusion occurs to the south of Aodann and consists of a feldspathic matrix containing small crystals of albite-perthite and xenoliths of basalt. It is cut by a quartz-dolerite sheet and by thin basic dykes, but its general affinities are unknown.

The acid and basic magmas of Ardnamurchan

The spatial and temporal association of acid and basic magmas is a characteristic feature of most of the plutonic intrusions of Centre 2. In several bodies it is also evident that the emplacement of the two magma types was roughly contemporaneous. A similar association of acid and basic magmas occurs in intrusions of Centre 3 (p. 59) and even Centre 1 (p. 22).

Wells (1954b) suggests that the acid material of the granophyric quartz-dolerite owes its origin to having separated from a crystallising basic parent under the influence of a sudden reduction of external pressure. In contrast Skelhorn and Elwell (1966) believe it more likely that the acid material was derived as a result of the fusion of Lewisian country rock. They also suggest that the high-alumina basalt (porphyritic dolerite) facies of the granophyric quartz-dolerite was formed from a tholeiitic magma under high water pressure, and that the variation in composition of the aphyric dolerite facies was produced by mixing of a tholeiitic magma with an acid magma. Similar arguments may apply to other members of the intrusive complex. In terms of magmatic evolution, Skelhorn and Elwell (1966) disagree with Richey et al. (1930), who consider that the tholeiitic magma was produced by removal of olivine from an alkali basalt magma, which in turn produced the acid series by fractionation. Kennedy (1933) also considers that the tholeiitic magma was the parent for the alkali basalt, acid and eucrite-allivalite magmas. Skelhorn and Elwell (1966), however, believe that the alkali basalt magma was the parent for the high alumina basalts (which formed by accumulation of a basic plagioclase), and (by further accumulation of olivine) the eucrite-allivalite series. Holland and Brown (1972) note that a gap occurs in the composition range of the cone-sheets of Ardnamurchan, closely comparable to that discussed by Thompson (1972). They suggest that this gap may be formed by plagioclase separation together with some olivine, a mechanism which would favour crystal/liquid fractionation rather than the mixing of basalt and locally derived granitic liquids. However, they also consider that in addition to a fractionation mechanism, contamination by Lewisian country rock may have occurred during the production of the cone-sheet magma.

It is apparent, therefore, that evidence exists which supports both fractionation of basaltic magma and the assimilation or fusion of country rock, as factors acting in the petrogenesis of the intrusive complex. There is also evidence which both supports and argues against the direct association of the various magma types. However, work by Gribble and O'Hara (1967) suggests that incorporation of country rock material in basic magmas can only be on a small scale, since experimental evidence from the system $CaO-MgO-Al_2O_3-SiO_2$ reveals the presence of several thermal divides which would tend to restrict any such assimilation process from operating on a large scale.

The cone-sheets of Centres 1, 2 and 3

Intrusion of the cone-sheets was preceded by a period of updoming. This produced an elongate structure in Mesozoic sediments and Tertiary volcanics which trends north-east to south-west across the centre of the complex. The majority of the cone-sheets are quite thin but they occur in vast numbers and may collectively form extensive outcrops, although individually they are usually of very limited arcuate extent. The cone-sheets are chiefly composed of non-porphyritic quartz-dolerite, porphyritic dolerite or porphyritic basalt, but composite cone-sheets occur in which the margins are typically quartz-dolerite, with more acid centres of craignurite, granophyre or felsite. In the chilled edges and fine-grained marginal zones of the porphyritic cone-sheets, phenocrysts are not usually developed. Individual cone-sheets appear to have been intruded successively, for they bear well-chilled margins whether in contact with country rock or with an earlier cone-sheet. Even within a small area of sheets of similar trend a long history of activity may be indicated by dykes both cutting and cut by the cone-sheets. Cone-sheet fractures appear to have been formed before the emplacement of the cone-sheet magma, as fracture planes lying parallel to the cone-sheets, yet not occupied by intrusive material, may be observed. Where injection has occurred displacement of the wall rock takes place in a vertical sense.

Richey *et al.* (1930) divide the cone-sheets of Centre 2 into an outer suite and an inner suite. The outer suite, which has affinities with the Centre 1 cone-sheets, is principally composed of non-porphyritic quartz-dolerite sheets inclined at angles of the order of 30°, and which pre-date the emplacement of the hypersthene-gabbro of Ardnamurchan Point. In contrast, the inner suite, which has affinities with Centre 3 cone-sheets, is mainly composed of porphyritic dolerite and porphyritic basalt sheets inclined at about 70°, which post-date the emplacement of the hypersthene-gabbro. The inner cone-sheets of Centre 2 pre-date the emplacement of the Beinn nan Ord eucrite, whereas the Centre 3 cone-sheets pre-date the Great Eucrite of Centre 3.

This simple pattern of an outer and inner series is further confused by the presence of members of the outer cone-sheet suite cutting the hypersthene-gabbro near An Acairseid, to the south-east of Beinn na Seilg, and near

Sanna Point, and the occurrence of non-porphyritic quartz-dolerite in the inner suite and porphyritic dolerite and porphyritic basalt in the outer suite.

Since many of the inner cone-sheets occur as isolated exposures, and have measured dips of 90° (observed by one of the authors, C.D.G., in the inner sheets about 1 km south-west of Achosnich), it is possible that some of the inner cone-sheets could be Tertiary basic dykes vertically intruded into the earlier igneous complexes.

The non-porphyritic quartz-dolerite cone-sheets are fine-grained rocks rich in iron ore and composed of a moderately basic plagioclase, augite, titanomagnetite, alkali feldspar of an albitic character, and quartz. They generally show a separation of the coarser grained and more basic components from an acid residuum, which was capable of migration and segregation into well-defined but unevenly distributed areas. The porphyritic cone-sheets are ordinary basalts and quartz-dolerites, containing phenocrysts of plagioclase.

Within the composite cone-sheets, the contact between basic and acid portions may be either sharp or gradational, or the two zones may be separated by a zone of intermediate composition which usually contains much altered and partly resolved basic xenoliths. Some of the felsitic centres may approach pitchstone in character, with the suggestion of an original glassy texture.

Holland and Brown (1972) state that chemically the cone-sheets cannot be subdivided into separate suites either in terms of their relative age of emplacement, or according to their disposition in relation to the three possible centres of magmatic activity. However, they have been able to provide evidence for the definition of a Hebridean tholeiitic series, but whether this series implies crystal fractionation of tholeiitic basalt magma, or mixing of this magma and a granitic melt derived by partial melting of crustal rocks, is uncertain. They do suggest, though, that tholeiitic basalt magma was available in large quantities during the Tertiary volcanism in north-west Scotland, shown by the formation of large, layered basic intrusions with tholeiitic affinities (Wager and Brown 1968); and that the cone-sheets may have originated by tapping of a basalt reservoir emplaced at fairly high levels within the crust, generally slightly later than the formation of the alkali basalt plateaux. Thus two Hebridean basalt magma series exist.

Since it is unlikely that the Ardnamurchan rocks differ from those of closely related complexes on Skye and Mull, then the strontium isotope data of Moorbath and Bell (1965) favours generation of the acid magmas chiefly from partial melting of the Precambrian crustal basement. Conversely, the lead isotope data of Moorbath and Welke (1969) shows extensive variation in the mixing proportions of younger upper mantle lead with ancient crustal lead in both acid and basic rocks, indicating that there is not only contamination of the basalts (alkali and tholeiitic), but the acid rocks appear to be a mixture of basalt differentiates and crustal remelts. In this context, Green and Wright (1969) note that, from the data given by Holland and Brown (1972), it appears that the cone-sheets of Centre 1 and those of Centre 2 near Mingary are the most silicic suggesting that this may be an area of late magmatic activity. It is also interesting to note that the progression from more basic to more acid is observed in small volcanic centres such as Glas Eilean (Paithankar 1967) and within most of the ring dykes of Centre 2 (Richey *et al.* 1930; Skelhorn and Elwell 1966).

Walker (1975) considers that the evolution of the Ardnamurchan igneous complex along with other Tertiary centres, is heralded by the rise of an acid diapir, which caused updoming of the overlying Mesozoic sediments and Tertiary basaltic volcanics, and preceded the rise of its parent basaltic magma. The emplacement of the cone-sheets is governed by a tendency of the rising magma to move in the direction of maximum excess hydrostatic pressure (see also Bradley 1965). No remains of this acid diapir are preserved on Ardnamurchan, so that the acid magma, if present, must have either been entirely ejected to form acid volcanics, or removed by erosion if it ever formed a high-level pluton.

In contrast to this hypothesis of almost passive emplacement of the cone-sheets, Phillips' (1974) concept involves the dynamic loading of the cover to a magma chamber by magmatic pressure. Sudden expansion of magma may give rise to the initiation of shear fractures at several levels on the shoulder of the magma chamber, which by upward extension would allow the central region of country rock, overlying the magma chamber, to rise. This would be accompanied by the opening of the shear fractures and the inflow of magma to form the cone-sheets, but Walker (1975, in discussion) points out that basalt magmas seem to be the least likely to exert localised pressures, and that no structures interpreted as the surface or near surface manifestation of cone-sheets have been described from modern basaltic volcanoes. Phillips' (1974) hypothesis does, however, explain the absence of cone-sheets from the zone of country rock near the apparent focus of any suite. This is one of the major objections to the mechanism of emplacement of the cone-sheets along tensile fractures originating from localised magmatic pressure, as proposed by Anderson (1936). Nevertheless, Phillips' (1974) hypothesis may also be criticised in terms of the periodic history of activity required to account for the cone-sheet development on Ardnamurchan, and the requirement that three independent yet intersecting fracture systems in close spatial and temporal proximity must have formed if the cone-sheets are considered to occur along fractures which are circular in plan.

Durrance (1967) suggests that the outcrop pattern of all the cone-sheets of the complex may be explained in terms of a single conjugate shear fracture system which originated from a centripetal stress field caused by a reduction in magmatic pressure, the fractures opening to admit the cone-sheets when magmatic pressure increased. Durrance (1967) also suggests that torsional stresses may accompany the emplacement of the cone-sheets along the fractures, determining whether sinistral or dextral shears open. In this context, it is interesting to note that the cone-sheets attributed to Centre 1 and the outer suite of Centre 2 largely occupy sinistral shears, and are generally composed of non-porphyritic quartz-dolerite, while the inner suite of Centre 2 cone-sheets and the cone-sheets of Centre 3 largely occupy dextral shears and are generally composed of porphyritic dolerite or porphyritic basalt. These divisions perhaps represent a broad grouping of the cone-sheets in order of intrusion.

CENTRE 3

Centre 3 is the youngest plutonic ring complex of Ardamurchan (Fig. 2) and forms the largest and most complete set of ring intrusions in the British Isles. Richey *et al.* (1930) regarded the rocks of this Centre as outward dipping ring dykes, becoming progressively younger towards the centre and formed by a process of cauldron subsidence. However, this model is not universally accepted and more recent studies have suggested inward dipping, funnel or saucer shapes for at least some of the intrusions of Centre 3. This account attempts to describe the geology of Centre 3 in the light of these recent studies, including work by Smith (1957), Bradshaw (1961), Wills (1970) and Walsh (1971). The rocks are mainly coarse-grained gabbros with the development of a relatively small volume of intermediate rocks in the centre of the complex. Since the structure of the complex is not known for certain, the descriptive term "ring intrusion" is used here in preference to the genetic term "ring dyke".

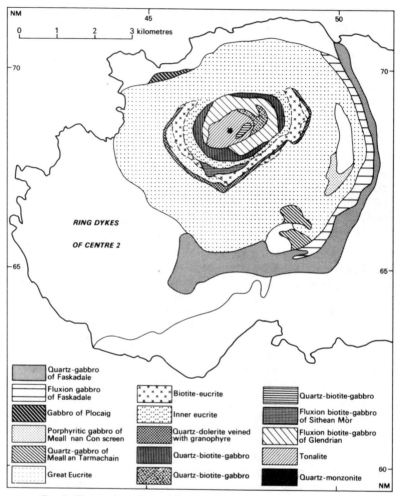

FIG. 8. The ring intrusions of Centre 3 (following Richey *et al.* 1930).

54

Intrusive plutonic rocks

The subdivisions of the rocks ascribed to Centre 3 are shown in Figure 8. It should be borne in mind that in many cases the sequence of intrusion is uncertain and, as is shown in the account, the divisions themselves are in some respects inadequate.

Quartz-gabbro of Faskadale

This is the outermost ring intrusion of Centre 3 and extends from Faskadale Bay south and then west around almost half the circumference of the complex (Fig. 8). It may also continue westwards under a roof of rocks of the Centre 2 ring complex to re-emerge south of Sanna Bay as the younger quartz-gabbro of Ben Bhuidhe (see p. 45).

The gabbro is typically composed of augite, zoned labradorite and substantial amounts of magnetite with small amounts of interstitial quartz and alkali feldspar. Table 4 gives approximate modal compositions for the Centre 3 rocks. An indication of the petrography of the representative samples of the quartz-gabbro of Faskadale is given in Table 4. However, the quartz-gabbro is a very variable rock in detail, and locally may range from an olivine-eucrite to a basic granophyre where an acid mesostasis has developed.

The outer contacts of the intrusion cut the outer cone-sheet complex and the Centre 2 ring intrusions in the south. However, the junction with the surrounding rocks cannot be located with sufficient accuracy to establish the shape of the intrusion.

Fluxion gabbro of Faskadale

The quartz-gabbro of Faskadale (Fig. 8) surrounds the fluxion gabbro of Faskadale, which occupies a narrow strip of country mainly to the west of the Allt Faskadale.

E

	EUCRITES	QUARTZ GABBROS	FLUXION GABBROS	DOLERITE	TONALITE	QUARTZ-MONZONITE
Plagioclase	64 (An 65-75)	52 (An 50-60)	51	57 (An 30)	39 (An 20-30)	36 (An 20-30)
Quartz + Alk. feldspar		2	2	3	*10/20	*10/28
Pyroxene	17	30	30	27	7	5
Olivine	16					
Biotite		2	2	4	8	9
Hornblende					4	4
Opaques	3	8	9	6	6	5
Accessories + Alteration		6	6	3	6	3

*Quartz/Alkali feldspar

Table 4.   Modal proportions of the Centre 3 rocks.

The values given are *very* approximate, especially for abundances below 10%. Some of the intrusions have insufficient data to give even approximate values.

Fluxion gabbro is common in Ardnamurchan and Richey *et al.* (1930) point out that this rock, like the other fluxion gabbros, has small amounts of biotite as a normal constituent. However, biotite can also be found in the quartz-gabbros, and there is very little difference in petrography between quartz-gabbros and fluxion gabbros. This is shown in Table 4, where the fluxion gabbro modal analysis would approximate to the mode of typical samples of the fluxion gabbro of Faskadale. The fluxion structure is regarded as evidence for injection of the mass in a semi-fluid condition. The fluxion planes dip at an angle of 20 to 40 degrees towards the focus of Centre 3. However, there is no direct evidence for the shape of the intrusion. Contacts between the fluxion gabbro and the outer quartz-gabbro are difficult to locate but the limited evidence available suggests the fluxion gabbro is the later (Richey *et al.* 1930).

Gabbro of Plocaig

This is a small mass on the margin of the Great Eucrite, which appears separate from, and older than, the Great Eucrite (Richey *et al.* 1930, p. 291).

Porphyritic gabbro of Meall nan Con screen

This is a small area of altered gabbro which is entirely surrounded by, and may be part of, the Great Eucrite (Bradshaw 1961). This conclusion is supported by analyses of this "gabbro" (Walsh 1971), which show differences in chemistry between the eucrites and the gabbros of Centre 3. The analyses from the porphyritic gabbro of Meall nan Con show greater similarities to the analyses from the eucrites.

Great Eucrite

The most prominent topographical feature of the area occupied by Centre 3 is the massive ring of the Great Eucrite (Fig. 8). This rock is highly resistant to weathering and occupies a ridge of high ground, producing a natural amphitheatre around the lower-lying area of the inner part of the complex. There is much evidence of glaciation with abundant *roches moutonnées* and glacial erratics. The Great Eucrite is by far the largest of the intrusions of Centre 3, representing over one half the total area of the exposed rocks.

Petrographically the Great Eucrite is typically a coarse feldspathic gabbroic rock containing both augite and olivine, the proportions of which can vary substantially, a representative modal composition being given in Table 4. The term eucrite has no unequivocal definition, generally being used for a gabbroic rock with a zoned calcic plagioclase near to bytownite in composition, and containing olivine and pyroxene, with subordinate iron ore and orthopyroxene. In a few localities orthopyroxene may be more abundant than clinopyroxene, but clinopyroxene usually predominates. Table 4 shows the major petrographic differences between the Great Eucrite and the quartz- and fluxion gabbros. In the field the higher concentration of plagioclase and the less abundant ore minerals give the eucrites a lighter colour. The presence of rusty coloured oxidation of the olivine is also frequently diagnostic of the eucrites. However, although typical eucrites and gabbros can readily be distinguished in the field, both rocks are very variable and in many places it is difficult to distinguish one from the other. The rocks surrounding the eucrite have in some places suffered contact alteration by the intrusion of the presumably later eucrite, but the eucrite itself shows no evidence of a chilled margin. Although contacts between the eucrite and the quartz- and fluxion gabbros of Faskadale are hard to find, the Great Eucrite is presumed to be the later intrusion but the evidence is not conclusive.

Biotite-eucrite and inner eucrite

These two "intrusions" may be conveniently considered together; and with the Great Eucrite. Richey *et al.* (1930)

separates the Great Eucrite, the biotite-eucrite, and the inner eucrite and suggests further separate zones (Harry and Richey 1963; Richey personal communication). However, Bradshaw (1961) and Smith (1957) from a detailed study conclude that the three eucrites are all part of a single intrusion, emplaced more or less at the same time. Bradshaw shows that biotite occurs sporadically throughout the eucrites but is not restricted to, nor always present in, the biotite-eucrite. He also suggests that the intrusion is funnel-shaped, rather than an outward dipping ring dyke.

Quartz-gabbro of Meall an Tarmachain summit

This small mass is considered by Richey et al. (1930) to be later than the surrounding eucrite. However, its relations with the surrounding rocks are hard to establish in the field.

A recent study of the clinopyroxene compositions from the rocks of Centre 3 (Walsh 1975) has shown that the pyroxenes of the Meall an Tarmachain gabbro are different from the pyroxenes of all the other Centre 3 gabbros. There is a substantial increase in the iron content of the clino-pyroxenes from this intrusion.

Quartz-dolerite veined with granophyre

There is within the Great Eucrite a narrow ring intrusion of quartz-dolerite veined by granophyre. This intrusion runs intermittently around half of the centre but, as with several other intrusions, dies out to the north-west. The granophyre occurs as small masses and as "net-veining" in the dolerite and a discussion of this feature is given in the Centre 2 account (p. 47). Table 4 shows that petrographically the dolerite can be distinguished from the gabbros and eucrites by the greater amount of biotite, and the more sodic composition of plagioclase feldspars. Unlike the gabbros and eucrites it is a very homogeneous rock, and is also finer grained. In the granophyre true granophyric texture is not common, and "microgranite" might be a better term. The intrusion of quartz-dolerite veined with granophyre was regarded by Richey *et al.* (1930) as the best example of a ring dyke in Centre 3, dipping outwards from the centre at about 70°. The dolerite portion was probably emplaced along a ring fracture, consolidated and then brecciated, before the emplacement of the "granophyre" along cracks and fissures. Despite its close association with so much basic material (granophyre forms less than 5% of the intrusion) the granophyre is a very acid rock with a silica content in excess of 72% even at the very contact with the dolerite (Walsh 1971). Gribble (1974) concludes, from a geochemical examination of this quartz-dolerite, that it is similar to the quartz-dolerite (also veined by granophyre) of Centre 2, but quite different from the quartz-dolerites of Centre 1.

Quartz-gabbros

The three quartz-gabbro masses of Centre 3 are presumed by Richey *et al.* (1930) to have originally been part of one intrusion which occupied the whole area of the inner part of the complex, which was subsequently intruded by later rocks. The outermost of the three masses forms an almost complete ring intrusion enclosed by the eucrites (Fig. 8). It occupies a low-lying area of country and is poorly exposed, by comparison with other members of Centre 3.

The quartz-gabbros are heterogeneous rocks showing considerable variations in the proportions of the different minerals present (Table 4 gives an average modal composition). The quartz-gabbros are frequently pegmatitic and in addition to the main mineral phases (plagioclase, augite and ore minerals) biotite is present, being here slightly more abundant than in the outer gabbros. The other minerals include alteration products which Wills

(1970) identifies as a "greenschist facies assemblage superimposed during a long period of cooling and auto-metasomatism".

Detailed mapping of the gabbro by Wills (1970) fails to establish unequivocally whether the outer margin (of the outermost intrusion) dips inwards or outwards, or whether the gabbro is younger than the surrounding eucrite. There is no evidence of a chilled margin to the gabbro and while it is *assumed* that it is post-eucrite it was presumably emplaced whilst the eucrite was still warm.

Fluxion gabbro of Glendrian

This intrusion is closely associated with the quartz-gabbros described above (Fig. 8). It forms a prominent topographical feature, is better exposed than the quartz-gabbros and has weathered out to form an "inner" ring within the major ring formed by the Great Eucrite.

Table 4 shows the mineralogy of typical fluxion gabbro to be very similar to that of the quartz-gabbro, although some increase in the amount of oxide minerals is often found.

The Glendrian fluxion gabbro almost certainly post-dates the surrounding quartz-gabbro, as it contains xenoliths of quartz-gabbro. The fluxioning structure has been mapped in detail by Wills (1970) and generally dips inward towards the centre at 30° to 45°. Contacts between the fluxion gabbro and quartz-gabbro cannot be located accurately, partly through lack of exposure, and partly because the fluxion structure is not always well developed.

Fluxion gabbro of Sìthean Mór

Richey *et al.* (1930) suggests that the fluxion gabbro of Sìthean Mór post-dates the three quartz-gabbros and pre-dates the fluxion gabbro of Glendrian. However, there is no evidence at all to show the age of the Sìthean Mór intrusion, relative to the two innermost gabbros, and it is best considered separately from those.

The Sìthean Mór gabbro is a crescent-shaped mass which is entirely surrounded by the eucrites (Fig. 8). Only the northern section of the intrusion is fluxioned. The southern portion is non-fluxioned and is a typical quartz-gabbro. The central part of the mass consists of inter banded layers of fluxion gabbro and quartz-gabbro.

The modal analyses given in Table 4, of quartz- and fluxion gabbros indicate the approximate compositions of the gabbros. The Sìthean Mór intrusion has a marginal apophysis to the south which contains xenoliths of the eucrite and establishes the post-eucrite age of the intrusion. In the middle of the intrusion the bands of fluxion gabbro and quartz-gabbro dip towards the centre at approximately 60°. In addition the fluxioning dips towards the centre at a steep angle (about 70°). *If* the fluxioning structure lies parallel to the margins of the Sìthean Mór intrusion, there is little doubt that this mass dips inwards, and not outwards as suggested by Richey *et al.* (1930).

Tonalite and quartz-monzonite

The last stage in the development of the rocks of Centre 3 was the formation of the distinctive tonalite and related quartz-monzonite, which occupy the centre of the area. Although not large the oval-shaped intrusions form one of the most extensive areas of intermediate plutonic rocks in the Scottish Tertiary Igneous Province.

In hand specimen the rocks are quite distinctive with biotite set in a feldspathic groundmass. In thin section the rocks contain plagioclase, alkali feldspar, quartz, augite, hornblende, biotite, magnetite, ilmenite, apatite and chlorite, indicating a disequilibrium assemblage. In the tonalite the grain size variations are significant and the outer, fine-grained and more acid portion is regarded as a chilled margin. Acid veins also extend into the surrounding gabbroic rocks in places. However, there are no signs of alteration to the surrounding gabbros at the margin of the tonalite. Definite contacts between tonalite and the gabbro are very hard to find. Wills (1970) suggests, on the basis of two contacts, that the outer contact of the tonalite dips steeply outwards. On the other hand two contacts, found at the margin of the quartz-monzonite with the tonalite, dip inwards at 65°. It is unlikely, though not impossible, that these two intrusions have substantially different shapes.

The small mass of quartz-monzonite is distinguished from the tonalite by its greater biotite content, which is present as large brown platy crystals. Table 4 gives the modal compositions of the tonalite and quartz-monzonite rocks.

The structure of Centre 3 and the importance of fluxion structures in the gabbros

One of the problems of Centre 3 which is still unresolved is whether the intrusions comprising the complex dip inwards or outwards. None of the recent studies has disproved the original concept that the intrusions are a series of outward dipping ring dykes (Richey *et al.* 1930) and the evidence from the quartz-dolerite veined with granophyre would certainly support this view. However, this is a relatively small intrusion, probably emplaced along a ring-fracture within the Great Eucrite, and it is quite possible that it has a different shape to the main ring intrusions.

On the other hand the fluxion structure of the three gabbro intrusions of Faskadale, Sìthean Mór and Glendrian suggests a funnel or saucer shape, assuming that the fluxioning structure is a flow phenomenon and lies parallel to the walls of the intrusion. However, this inference may be quite invalid, since examination of modern lava flows show that the fluxion banding and the boundary of the flows are not invariably parallel. The limited evidence from the contacts of the intrusions suggests that the Centre is funnel-shaped rather than the conventional "ring-dyke" structure.

The term fluxion gabbro is used by Richey *et al.* (1930) to describe gabbros in Ardnamurchan where there is alignment of the plagioclase feldspar crystals in one particular direction. The fluxion structure was considered to have been produced by flow within the magma that subsequently crystallised to form the various fluxion gabbros. Thus the term has both descriptive and genetic implications. The problem that remains unresolved is whether the fluxioning is parallel to the sides of the intrusions (in which case there is little doubt that the intrusions of Centre 3 dip inwards).

It is considered significant that in Centre 3 fluxion gabbro invariably follows and is closely associated with non-fluxion gabbro. The fluxion gabbro of Faskadale follows the quartz-gabbro of Faskadale, and indeed in places the two cannot be separated in the field. Richey *et al.* (1930, p. 289) regard them as separate intrusions but found only one apparent contact between the two intrusions. The Sìthean Mór intrusion is part quartz-gabbro and part fluxion gabbro with the central portion a mixture of fluxion and non-fluxion gabbro. Typical hand specimens of the fluxion biotite-gabbro of Glendrian can be distinguished from the surrounding quartz-gabbro, but Richey *et al.* (1930, p. 334) note that "in the field their line of separation is sometimes difficult to determine".

There is no substantial difference in modal petrography between Centre 3 fluxion and non-fluxion gabbros (Table 4), and there is also no discernible difference in their major or trace element chemistry (Walsh 1971). Nor can any difference in mineral chemistry be detected. Walsh (1975) showed very similar clinopyroxene compositions for all the main gabbro intrusions (Fig. 9).

It is therefore tentatively suggested that the fluxion gabbros represent the later stages in the emplacement of the gabbro intrusions. The fluxioning structure was formed by movement of the magma in a semi-solid condition, as a crystal mush. If this hypothesis is correct, then the fluxion structure indicates the direction of movement of the magma, and hence it would be reasonable to conclude that the intrusions dip inwards.

The petrogenesis of the rocks of Centre 3

It has now been demonstrated that all the basic rocks of Centre 3, the eucrites, the gabbros, and the dolerite, are closely related and form three separate and distinct groups of rocks which are part of a fractionation sequence (Walsh 1975). Analyses of clinopyroxenes from the three eucrites show only a very small range of compositions, as do clino-pyroxenes from the Centre 3 gabbro intrusions. No discernible differences could be found between the "outer" gabbros of Faskadale and the "inner" gabbros of Sìthean Mór and Glendrian. No differences are seen in clino-pyroxene compositions from fluxion and non-fluxion gabbros (Fig. 9). However, when the compositions of the gabbroic clinopyroxenes are compared with the eucritic clinopyroxenes there is a significant increase in Fe/Mg ratio. This systematic increase in Fe/Mg ratio continues for the dolerite of Centre 3, which shows a substantial iron enrichment relative to the gabbros. This trend in pyroxene compositions is comparable to other fractionated tholeiitic intrusions such as the Skaergaard intrusion of E. Greenland (Muir 1951; Brown 1957; Brown and Vincent 1963), and the Bushveld intrusion of South Africa (Atkins 1969). The Ardnamurchan clinopyroxenes also show changes in the concentrations of other elements such as a

65

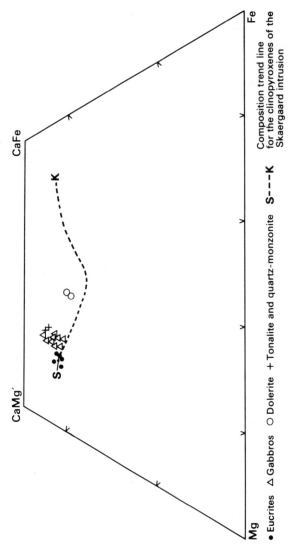

Fig. 9. Compositions of clinopyroxenes from rocks of Centre 3. Clinopyroxenes from the eucrites are less iron-rich than clinopyroxenes from the gabbros, and clinopyroxenes from the dolerite show substantial iron enrichment. The trend is similar to the Skaergaard trend although with less calcium depletion. The samples from the tonalite and quartz-monzonite do not continue this iron enrichment trend, and are interpreted as hybrid rocks formed from the partial melting of pre-existing rocks by the basic magma. Samples from the small gabbro intrusion of Meall an Tarmachain have been omitted as their results are ambiguous.

Mg

• Eucrites △ Gabbros ○ Dolerite + Tonalite and quartz-monzonite   **S – – K**   Composition trend line for the clinopyroxenes of the Skaergaard intrusion

CaMg'

CaFe

Fe

fall in the Cr and Ni contents. In addition the composition of biotites from Centre 3 gabbros and dolerite show the Fe/Mg ratio increasing from the gabbro to the dolerite.

Nevertheless, these changes, which are characteristic of a tholeiitic fractionation sequence, are not found in the intermediate rocks, namely the tonalite and the quartz-monzonite. The Fe/Mg ratio of the clinopyroxenes from these intermediate rocks decreases instead of increasing and is substantially less than in clinopyroxenes of the dolerite (Fig. 9). Furthermore the biotites from the tonalite and quartz-monzonite have lower Fe contents than biotites from either the dolerite or even the gabbros.

These results demonstrate that in Centre 3 all the basic rocks are closely related and represent three stages in the fractionation of basic magma. The tonalite and quartz-monzonite in the very centre of the complex cannot have formed by continued fractionation of the magma and instead are interpreted as hybrids formed by the partial remelting and assimilation of country rocks into basic magma.

REFERENCES

Anderson, E. M. 1936. The dynamics of the formation of cone-sheets, ring dykes and cauldron-subsidences. *Proc. R. Soc. Edinb.* **56**, 128-157.

Atkins, F. B. 1969. The pyroxenes of the Bushveld intrusion, S. Africa. *J. Petrology.* **10**, 222-249.

Bailey, E. B., and Maufe, H. B. 1916. The geology of Ben Nevis and Glen Coe. *Mem. geol. Surv. U.K.*

Bailey, E. B. *et al.* 1924. The Tertiary and post-Tertiary geology of Mull, Loch Aline and Oban. *Mem. geol. Surv. U.K.*

Bott, M. H. P. and Tuson, J. 1973. The deep structure beneath the Tertiary volcanic regions of Skye, Mull and Ardnamurchan. *Nature, Phys. Sci. Lond.* **242**, 114-116.

Bradshaw, N. 1961. The mineralogy and petrology of the eucrites of the Centre 3 igneous complex, Ardnamurchan, Scotland. *Ph.D. Thesis Univ. Manchr* (unpubl.).

Brown, G. M. 1954. A suggested igneous origin for the banded granular hornfelses within the hypersthene-gabbro of Ardnamurchan, Argyllshire, *Mineralog. Mag.* **30**, 529-533.

Brown, G. M. 1957. Pyroxenes from the early and middle stages of fractionation of the Skaergaard intrusion, E. Greenland, *Mineralog. Mag.* **31**, 511-543.

Brown, G. M. and Vincent, E. A. 1963. Pyroxenes from the late stages of fractionation of the Skaergaard intrusion, E. Greenland. *J. Petrology* **4**, 175-197.

Butchins, C. S. 1973. An extension of the granophyric quartz-dolerite intrusion of Centre 2, Ardnamurchan, Argyllshire. *Geol. Mag.* **110**, 473-475.

Durrance, E. M. 1967. Photoelastic stress studies and their application to a mechanical analysis of the Tertiary ring complex of Ardnamurchan, Argyllshire. *Proc. Geol. Ass.* **78**, 289-318.

Geikie, A. 1897. *Ancient volcanoes of Great Britain.* v. **2.** London.

Green, J. and Wright, J. B. 1969. Ardnamurchan, Centre 1, does it need redefining? *Geol. Mag.* **106,** 599-601.

Green, J. and Wright, J. B. 1974. Ardnamurchan, Centre 1 — new radiometric evidence. *Geol. Mag.* **111,** 163-164.

Gribble, C. D. 1974. The dolerites of Ardnamurchan. *Scott. J. Geol.* **10,** 71-89.

Gribble, C. D. and O'Hara, M. J. 1967. Interaction of basic magma with pelitic materials. *Nature, Lond.* **217.**

Harry, W. T. and Richey, J. E. 1963. Magmatic pulses in the emplacement of plutons. *Lpool Manch. geol. J.* **3,** 254-268.

Holland, J. G. and Brown, G. M. 1972. Hebridean tholeiitic magmas: a geochemical study of the Ardnamurchan cone-sheets. *Contr. Mineral. Petrol.* **37,** 139-160.

Kennedy, W. Q. 1933. Trends of differentiation in basaltic magmas. *Am. J. Sci.* **25,** 239-256.

Kuenen, Ph. H. 1937. Intrusion of cone-sheets. *Geol. Mag.* **74,** 177-183.

Le Bas, M. J. 1971. Cone-sheets as a mechanism of uplift. *Geol. Mag.* **108,** 373-376.

Macintyre, R. M., McMenamin, T. and Preston, J. 1975. K-Ar results from Western Ireland and their bearing on the timing and siting of Thulean magmatism. *Scott. J. Geol.* **11,** 227-250.

McQuillin, R., Bacon, M. and Binns, P. E. 1975. The Blackstones Tertiary igneous complex. *Scott. J. Geol.* **11,** 179-192.

Mitchell, J. G. and Reen, K. P. 1973. Potassium-argon ages from the Tertiary ring complexes of the Ardnamurchan peninsula, western Scotland. *Geol. Mag.* **110,** 331-340.

Moorbath, S. and Bell, J. D. 1965. Strontium abundance isotope studies and rubidium-strontium age determinations on Tertiary rocks from the Isle of Skye, northwest Scotland. *J. Petrology* **6**, 37-66.

Moorbath, S. and Welke, H. 1969. Lead isotope studies on igneous rocks from the Isle of Skye, northwest Scotland. *Earth Planet. Sci. Lett.* **5**, 217-230.

Muir, I. D. 1951. The clinopyroxenes of the Skaergaard intrusion, N. Greenland, *Mineralog. Mag.* **29**, 690-714.

Paithankar, M. G. 1967. Tuffisite and volcanic phenomena associated with the Glas Eilean vent, Ardnamurchan, Argyllshire, Scotland. *Geol. For. Stockh. Forh.* **89**, 15-28.

Paithankar, M. G. 1968. Petrological study and intrusion history of the granophyre of Grigadale and associated gabbros, Ardnamurchan, Argyllshire, Scotland. *Neues. Jb. Miner. Abh.* **110**, 1-23.

Phillips, W. J. 1974. The dynamic emplacement of cone-sheets. *Tectonophysics* **24**, 69-84.

Reynolds, D. L. 1954. Fluidization as a geological process, and its bearing on the problem of intrusive granites. *Am. J. Sci.* **252**, 577-613.

Richey, J. E. 1933. Summary of the geology of Ardnamurchan. *Proc. Geol. Ass.* **44**, 1-56.

Richey, J. E., Thomas, H. H. *et al.* 1930. The geology of Ardnamurchan, north-west Mull and Coll. *Mem. geol. Surv. U.K.*

Richey, J. E. and MacGregor, A. G. 1961. Scotland: The Tertiary volcanic districts. *Br. reg. Geol.* H.M.S.O.

Skelhorn, R. R. and Elwell, R. W. D. 1966. The structure and form of the granophyric quartz-dolerite intrusion, Centre 2, Ardnamurchan, Argyllshire. *Trans. R. Soc. Edinb.* **66**, 285-306.

Skelhorn, R. R. and Elwell, R. W. D. 1971. Central subsidence in the layered hypersthene-gabbro of Centre 2, Ardnamurchan, Argyllshire. *Jl geol. Soc. Lond.* **127**, 535-551.

Smith, D. I. 1957. The structure and petrology of the third

ring dyke complex, Ardnamurchan. *Ph.D. Thesis, Univ. Edinb.* (unpubl.).

Thompson, R. N. 1972. Evidence for a chemical discontinuity near the basalt-andesite transition in many anorogenic volcanic suites. *Nature, Lond.* **236**, 106-110.

Wager, L. R. and Brown, G. M. 1968. *Layered igneous rocks.* Edinburgh.

Walker, G. P. L. 1975. A new concept of the evolution of the British Tertiary intrusive centres. *Jl geol. Soc. Lond.* **131**, 121-141.

Walsh, J. N. 1971. The geochemistry and mineralogy of the Centre 3 igneous complex, Ardnamurchan, Argyllshire, Scotland. *Ph.D. Thesis, Univ. London* (unpubl.).

Walsh, J. N. 1975. Clinopyroxenes and biotites from the Centre 3 igneous complex, Ardnamurchan, Argyllshire. *Mineralog. Mag.* **40,** 335-345.

Wells, M. K. 1951. Sedimentary inclusions in the hypersthene-gabbro, Ardnamurchan, Argyllshire. *Mineralog. Mag.* **29**, 715-736.

Wells, M. K. 1954a. The structure and petrology of the hypersthene-gabbro intrusion, Ardnamurchan, Argyllshire. *Q. Jl geol. Soc. Lond.* **109,** 367-397.

Wells, M. K. 1954b. The structure of the granophyric quartz-dolerite intrusion of Centre 2, Ardnamurchan, and the problem of net-veining. *Geol. Mag.* **91,** 293-307.

Wells, M. K. and McRae, D. G. 1969. Palaeomagnetism of the hypersthene-gabbro intrusion, Ardnamurchan, Scotland. *Nature, Lond.* **223**, 608-609.

Wills, K. J. A. 1970. The inner complex of Centre 3, Ardnamurchan. *B.Sc. Thesis R. Sch. Mines, Univ. London* (unpubl.).

Wilson, N. S. 1973. Western Ardnamurchan. Camas-Inas, Salen-Sunart, Ardnamurchan. Private publn.

F

EXCURSIONS

The object of the excursion section is to provide an opportunity to examine the geology of Ardnamurchan in the field. Excursions of each of the three centres of Tertiary igneous activity are described, and attempts made to provide details of relationships both between intrusions of different centres and between intrusions belonging to the same centre. To complete the whole itinerary of field trips at least 7 days are needed, but if only a limited time is available then it is recommended that excursion 1 (sections A and B) and excursion 7 be attempted (2 days in all) with excursion 5 added if a "long weekend" of 3 days is available for field trips. Diagrams in this section, or given earlier in the main geology account, will provide details to complement the excursion accounts, and the coloured map should always be used. The Ordnance Survey 1:50,000 sheet 47 of the region will provide additional details of topography to supplement those given on the coloured map. Six-figure National Grid references are given for each excursion locality.

EXCURSION 1: Ormsaigbeg to Mingary Castle

This excursion provides an opportunity to examine the Mesozoic sediments, Tertiary basalts and Moine schists which are host to the intrusive complex. Also present are a variety of composite intrusions, some possibly related to Centre 1 activity, others comprising part of the Centre 2 cone-sheet and sill suite. In this area is developed possibly the most spectacular series of cone-sheets to be seen in the British Isles. Apart from the composite members these are mostly non-porphyritic quartz-dolerites, although a few porphyritic dolerites are also present. Early and late dykes of a variety of types are found both cutting and cut by the

72

cone-sheets. To take full advantage of the exposures available on this excursion the localities around Mingary Pier, Glas Eilean and Mingary Castle should be visited at low tide.

Total distance (Kilchoan-Kilchoan) about 18 km, although about half of this distance can be travelled by car.

Section A

From Kilchoan, where parking is possible opposite the access to the old jetty by the shops, follow the road south-west to Ormsaigbeg and thence along the coast path for about 300 m until access is afforded to the shore via a small headland. Figure 10 shows the geology of the area in detail.

Loc. 1 [465623]. The small headland consists of a massive quartz-dolerite dyke which trends north-west, flanked on either side by granophyre. Although the contact between these components in some places is sharp, it is more frequently indistinct, with brecciation of the basic rock and intrusion by acid veins. Extensive hybridization between the two components also occurs, best seen above the face forming the south-west side of the headland. As a composite intrusion it is unusual in that the acid material occupies a marginal relationship with respect to the earlier basic component.

Note

Exposures along the coast to the west of the small headland may be reached only at low tide, and therefore cannot form an integral part of the whole excursion. However, the area may be visited separately. Some parts of the coast are difficult to negotiate.

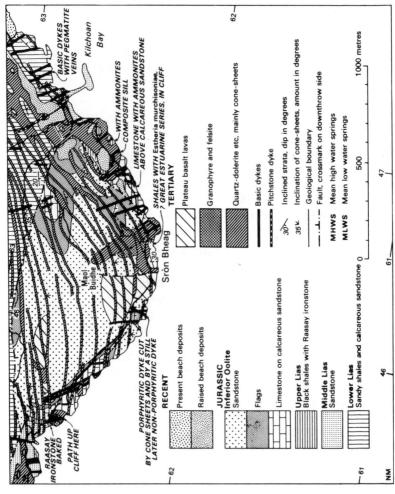

FIG. 10. The Mesozoic rocks and Tertiary igneous rocks of Sròn Bheag (based on Richey *et al.* 1930).

74

Loc. 1A [465623]. In the cliff immediately to the west of the western granophyre of the small headland, shales are present which may be part of the Great Estuarine Series.

Loc. 1B [461623]. In the bay to the north-west of the main headland of Sròn Bheag the sedimentary succession at shore level consists of sandstones, flags and limestones of Inferior Oolite age. Higher in the cliff a Tertiary basalt is found. Immediately beneath this basalt a mudstone, with a thin ironstone band, overlies a white sandstone. Both these sediments are probably of Tertiary age. Interesting age relationships between dykes and cone-sheets are present on the shore, where a north-north-east trending porphyritic basalt dyke cuts the Mesozoic sediments and is, in turn, cut by quartz-dolerite cone-sheets. Both dyke and cone-sheets have then been cut by a xenolithic non-porphyritic quartz-dolerite dyke.

Loc. 1C [455626]. Continue north-westwards for about 750 m across the Bajocian sediments (Inferior Oolite Series), which are cut by an early composite dyke and by many cone-sheets of the outer suite of Centre 2. Just after crossing an acid intrusion, Toarcian shales (U. Lias) outcrop with the Raasay Ironstone. This is about 1 m thick and largely altered to magnetite, but the remains of belemnites are still preserved. Return to Ormsaigbeg by retracing the outward route, as the cliff path marked in Figure 10 is hazardous.

Loc. 2 [467624]. From the large composite intrusion proceed north-eastwards for about 250 m to reach the lower part of the Inferior Oolite Series. This consists of limestones overlying calcareous sandstones. The limestones are fossiliferous, yielding belemnites and ammonites.

Loc. 3 [469625]. Follow the outcrop of the Inferior Oolite Series to the north-east to the point where the sediments are cut by a composite sheet. This has well-defined basic margins about 0.5 m thick and an acid interior measuring about 2 m across. The margins consist of fairly basic quartz-dolerite, while the interior is a far more acid quartz-dolerite. The central part of the sheet is locally highly xenolithic.

Loc. 4 [470626]. Continue north-eastwards along the coast for about 100 m. Just to the south-west of a marked ridge formed by an easterly dipping quartz-dolerite sheet, dark shales occur as lenticular patches within a cone-sheet complex. These shales are of Toarcian age and yield ammonites of the *Harpoceras falciferum* zone. Within the shales is found an oolitic limey ironstone. Like that seen to the west of Sròn Bheag, this is also correlated with the Raasay Ironstone.

Loc. 5 [471628]. Cross the quartz-dolerite ridge and then a wide pebble beach to fine-grained white sandstone of Domerian age (Scalpa Sandstone) which occurs in disconnected outcrops near low water mark. In this area a porphyritic dolerite dyke trending north-westerly is seen to be continuous with a cone-sheet of the same type. A pitchstone dyke cuts this cone-sheet; it has glassy margins free from spherulites and a banded spherulitic glass interior. Porphyritic dolerite cone-sheets predominate to the west and inland of this locality, while to the east they are mainly non-porphyritic.

Loc. 6 [473629]. North-eastwards towards the old jetty at Kilchoan, sandy micaceous shales occur with occasional calcareous sandstones representative of the Lower Pliensbachian (Pabba Beds). The beds dip to the south at about 30°, the structure forming part of the elongate dome which trends north-eastwards across the centre of the complex. Amongst many acid and basic dykes which cut these shales, a 10 m thick north-west trending olivine-dolerite, which occurs about 200 m north-east of the pebble beach near Loc. 5, is of significance. This dyke is cut by pink aplite/pegmatite veins and contains amygdales which consist of a lining of perthite, and a centre of prehnite, separated by a zone of small colourless garnets.

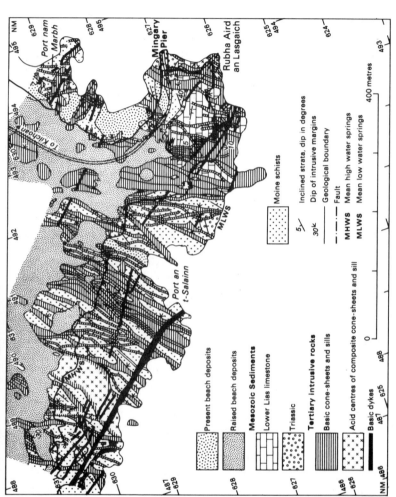

FIG. 11. The outer cone-sheets of Centre 2, Mingary Pier area (based on Richey *et al.* 1930).

Section B

At the site of the old jetty regain the main road and proceed eastwards. Just before the Kilchoan Hotel turn right towards Mingary Pier, where vehicles may be parked. Gain access to the shore south of the pier by means of the gate adjacent to the ferry house. Figure 11 shows the geology of the area south and west of the pier and Figure 4 the geology around Glas Eilean.

Loc. 7 [494626]. About 60 m south of the pier the lower half of a composite sill is visible, the upper half being cut off by a massive basic sill probably connected with the cone-sheets. The best exposure is below and to the east of the basic sill. The composite sill consists of a basic quartz-dolerite margin about 0.5 m thick, chilled externally against the host rock, and internally showing both sharp and gradational contacts with a granophyre. The internal junction shows no chilling effects. The granophyre contains abundant, more or less rounded, basic xenoliths which are characteristic of the marginal zone. These become smaller and more leucocratic away from the margin, with the centre of the granophyre practically free of inclusions.

Loc. 8 [493626]. Cross over the massive basic sill to the southern extremity of the shore some 150 m from the pier, where a cone-sheet about 7 m thick exhibits composite structure. The outer 2 m on both sides consists of a coarse-textured, spheroidally weathering rock and well-chilled margins. The internal 3 m exhibits vertical jointing with the centre containing a lenticular xenolithic mass. The outer and inner sections are both composed of fairly basic quartz-dolerite, but the xenolithic centre is a more acid quartz-dolerite. The xenoliths are mainly Moine schists, which develop a reaction rim of augite and quartz. In the calcareous shales overlying this intrusion, contact metamorphism has resulted in the growth of garnet, clino-pyroxene, idocrase, tremolite and prehnite.

Loc. 9 [492627]. Continue westwards for about 100 m to, a rocky/pebble bay just south of the cairn. In the small face above the high water mark, fractures parallel to the adjacent cone-sheets are seen cutting the L. Lias sediments in which thin limestones occur. The beds of limestone can be easily followed across the fractures, showing that no vertical displacement has occured along them. Elsewhere, fractures ocupied by cone-sheets show displacement of the walls in a vertical sense. On the shore below this exposure an early dyke of big-feldspar basalt can be found, crowded with phenocrysts of labradorite up to a few centimetres long, and cut by cone-sheets which are chilled against it.

Loc. 10 [484628]. Follow the coast north-westwards for about 700 m across a complex of cone-sheets, sills and dykes cutting the Moine schists to the pebble beach of Port na Luinge. Thence turn south and cross to the small tidal island of Glas Eilean (a clear path through the seaweed is present near the highest part of the beach). Vent agglomerate is well displayed on the island, fault-bounded against basalt on its northern and western margins, but with the original vent walls preserved to the south and east, where the host rock consists of Moine schists cut by quartz-dolerite cone-sheets. The agglomerate contains blocks of Moine schist, basalt, Jurassic limestone, sandstone and shale, as well as quartz-dolerite. The fragments are mostly angular and thoroughly mixed, with acid tuff infilling all the cracks and crevices. Acid veining occurs over a moderate area near the central part of the eastern margin. Fragments of acid rock are found in the agglomerate near the southern end of the western margin, which are possibly parts of an earlier composite cone-sheet. Ash occurs above high water mark in the central part of the outcrop near the southern shore.

Loc. 11 [485630]. Return to the mainland and follow the high water line along the eastern shore to a point about 100 m from Port na Luinge and the reappearance of a north-easterly extension of the Glas Eilean vent agglomerate. Here, the eastern margin is fault-bounded against Moine schists cut by quartz-dolerite cone-sheets, while the western margin against basalt appears to be the original vent wall. The features of the agglomerate are similar to those seen on Glas Eilean, but the central part of this outcrop, occupying a rather flat topographic area below high water mark, shows the presence of a tuffisite dyke cutting the agglomerate. A fluxion structure parallel to the walls is present within the dyke, and contacts with the agglomerate may be either sharp or gradational. Inclusions of fragments of agglomerate are common. Evidence of emplacement in a fluidized system is apparent. The vent is considered to be related to Centre 2 principally from the parallelism of its trend with the adjacent Centre 2 cone-sheets.

Section C

Return to Mingary Pier and thence to Kilchoan. By the Kilchoan Hotel turn right for Salen and after about 1 km right again for Mingary Farm and Mingary Castle. Vehicles should be parked on the left of the road before crossing the cattle grid. Follow the direction signs for Mingary Castle. The castle, now in a ruined condition (although some restoration work has recently been carried out), was originally the stronghold of the MacIans of Ardnamurchan. James IV received submission of the Island Chiefs here in 1493 and 1495. Beseiged by MacDonald of Lochalsh in 1517 and by Maclean of Duart in 1588, the castle passed to the Campbells under the Earl of Argyll in 1625. Acquired by James Riddell of Riddell Lodge, Berwickshire, in 1760, it was still roofed and habitable in the mid 19th century (Wilson 1973). Access to the shore may be achieved through the castle. Figure 12 shows the geology of the area.

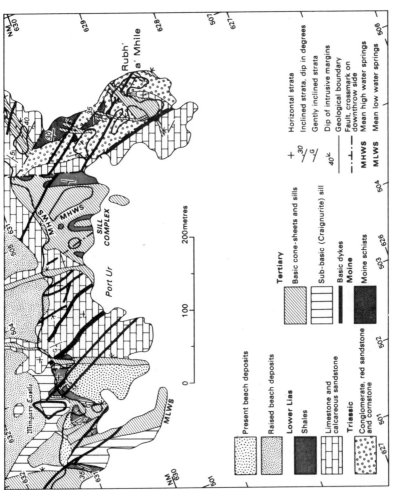

FIG. 12. Geology of the shore area near Mingary Castle (based on Richey et al. 1930).

81

Loc. 12 [503631]. A thick sheet consisting of a greenish-grey rock of granophyric type occurs beneath Mingary Castle. The rock is similar to the acid craignurites of Mull, and is thus considered to be a granophyre of craignurite affinity.

Loc. 13 [504630]. Continue eastwards along the shore where L. Lias limestones showing honeycomb weathering and containing shaly layers pass upwards into L. Lias shales. The shales are cut by a multiple quartz-dolerite sill complex.

Loc. 14 [506629]. If the tide is suitable, cross to the tidal islands of Rubha a' Mhìle. On the eastern side of the northern island, below high water mark, Triassic red sandstone and conglomerate about 6 m thick can be seen resting on Moine schists with the development of a basal breccia. Both the Moine schists and Triassic sediments are cut by north trending cone-sheets, which themselves are cut by a north-west trending basic dyke. At the southern end of the southern island, a Triassic cornstone is overlain by a pebbly sandstone. This sandstone, in turn, is overlain by white sandstone and sandy limestone of L. Lias age. The L. Lias sediments are cut by a quartz-dolerite sill which can be traced into a cone-sheet, to the north-east, with a north-east trend. This sill/cone-sheet cuts a north-westerly basic dyke, but is itself cut by a north trending cone-sheet.

EXCURSION 2: Kilchoan, Beinn na Seilg and Aodann

The objectives of this excursion are to examine around Kilchoan the effects of thermal alteration both in the host rocks and the included xenoliths of the hypersthene-gabbro of Centre 2, and to observe the relative age relationships and form of the plutonic intrusions of Centre 2 between Beinn na Seilg and Aodann. The internal structure of the hypersthene-gabbro and its contact with the granophyric quartz-dolerite are well displayed on the southern and eastern slopes of Beinn na Seilg, while the relationships between the eucrite of Beinn nan Ord and the quartz-gabbros of Beinn na Seilg, Garbh-dhail and Faskadale (Centre 3) are seen on the northern and western slopes. Cone-sheets of the inner suite of Centre 2 cut the quartz-gabbro of Garbh-dhail, and the contact of this ring dyke with the older gabbro of Lochan an Aodainn can be observed. The composite nature of the quartz-gabbro of Aodann is also well displayed. A late felsite is seen cutting the Aodann quartz-gabbro, and a pitchstone dyke cuts the hypersthene-gabbro.

Total distance (Kilchoan-Kilchoan) about 17 km, including car travel.

Section A

From the Kilchoan Hotel follow the main road westwards for about 300 m. Vehicles may be parked near the post office.

Loc. 1 [485637]. Just beyond the War Memorial, a small roadside exposure reveals amygdaloidal basalt. Although not suitable for collecting material, it is possible to observe that some thermal alteration has occurred, from the presence of a grey weathering product (as opposed to the normal rusty weathering of unaltered basalt). This is probably produced by the hypersthene-gabbro which is some 400 m to the north. A cone-sheet which cuts the basalt sill shows its dark, fine-grained margin.

Loc. 2 [481641]. Continue west along the main road, turn right for the lighthouse and proceed as far as the Free Church, where vehicles may be parked. In small exposures above the road, just to the south of the Free Church manse, the cone-sheets can be seen to still possess their dark margins although lying close to the hypersthene-gabbro.

The L. Lias shales which form the host to the cone-sheets are, however, considerably indurated.

Loc. 3 [479643]. Further north, immediately beyond the last house on the right of the road, recrystallised cone-sheets with a new growth of biotite are exposed cutting altered basalts, the amygdales in the basalts being filled with chlorite or plagioclase feldspar. Unaltered porphyritic cone-sheets with well-chilled margins are also present. These may be either part of the inner suite of Centre 2 or part of the Centre 3 suite.

Loc. 4 [480647]. Follow the lighthouse road north to the junction for Sanna. Turn right and proceed as far as the permanent caravan site, just before reaching the bridge over the Amhainn Chrò Bheinn. Limited parking is possible on the left of the road by the bridge. Joining the road by the entrance to the caravan site is a grassy track. Follow this track, which eventually gives way to a footpath, upstream for about 400 m, until a heavily hammered area on the path is reached. Black xenoliths in which dark green spinel, basic plagioclase, colourless corundum and sapphire occur, are found here as irregular shaped or rounded masses enclosed in a grey, completely recrystallised basic rock. This dark-grey rock is possibly an early consolidated part of the hypersthene-gabbro. A narrow, banded reaction zone, usually only a few centimetres wide, is developed between the sapphire-bearing masses and the grey rock. Normal hypersthene-gabbro occurs a few metres to the north of this locality, while the basalt of Glebe Hill which forms a roof to the gabbro, lies immediately to the south.

Section B

Return to the junction of the Sanna road with the Lighthouse road and turn right. Continue along the road for about 1.5 km to a point near the southern end of Lochan na Crannaig, where vehicles may be parked in a lay-by on the left of the road. Head south-westwards across country for about 500 m, using the slightly higher ground to skirt to the north-west of a large area of peat, then south-south-east for a further 400 m to the gorge of the Allt Fhearghais (not named on coloured map). Follow the stream southwards for about 700 m to the col between Beinn na Seilg and Stacan Dubha, and thence to the Lochain Ghleann Locha. Proceed to the western end of the strip of land separating the lochs, to examine relationships between the hypersthene-gabbro, basalt and a pitchstone dyke.

Loc. 5 [463638]. The outer contact of the hypersthene-gabbro passes between the lochs, lying in a hollow, bounded to the south by basalt. Judging by the topographic relationships, the contact dips fairly steeply. Cutting the hypersthene-gabbro is a north-north-west trending pitch-stone dyke. This is fairly well exposed near the western end of the south shore of the northern loch, the outcrop displaying the flow-banding characteristic of this particular intrusion.

Loc. 6 [462638]. Immediately west of the twin lochs, outcrops of basalt and hypersthene-gabbro occur in close proximity. Again the evidence suggests a steeply dipping contact. In this general area both the hypersthene-gabbro and the basalt are cut by cone-sheets of the outer suite of Centre 2.

Loc. 7 [462641]. The col separating Beinn na Seilg and Stacan Dubha has a central ridge of higher ground, with a gully (occupied by the Allt Fhearghais) to the east, and a more gentle depression to the west (this lies due north of the western end of the twin lochs). Head northwards to this depression. Near the highest point of the col, on its western flank, are several outcrops of the pitchstone dyke. Most of these show magnificent examples of contorted flow-banding. Nearby, in the centre of the col depression, dyke-

85

like bodies of fine-grained basic rock are present in the hypersthene-gabbro.

Loc. 8 [464641]. Skirt around to the south of the ridge of ground east of the col depression and cross the floor of the gully to Stacan Dubha. On the south-west hillside, over-looking the twin lochs, numerous xenolithic bands occur within the hypersthene-gabbro. The bands reach up to 1 m or so across, and keep a constant width for several metres before dying out. They usually dip northwards at about 25°, lying parallel to a mineralogical layering which is developed in the surrounding gabbro. Lithologically, they are dark grey, fine-grained basic rocks, and close in composition to the hypersthene-gabbro itself. Both the xenoliths and surrounding gabbro are cut by a system of acid veins.

Loc. 9 [465642]. Just a few metres north of the summit cairns of Stacan Dubha, steeply dipping dyke-like bodies of fine-grained basic rock usually only a few centimetres, but reaching up to 1 m thick, are found to extend through the hypersthene-gabbro for several metres. Some of these appear to have been intruded into the gabbro while the host was still hot, but others are definitely xenolithic.

Loc. 10 [466643]. Lying about 150 m north-east of the summit of Stacan Dubha is a marked north-north-west to south-south-east trending gully. North of this gully a number of gabbro-pegmatite bodies occur sporadically within the hypersthene-gabbro. Some of these pegmatites have associated cores of quartz-feldspar rock.

Loc. 11 [464643]. Follow the north side of the hill westwards to the crags which overlie the gully of the Allt Fhearghais, and form the north-western flank of the hill. A granophyre sheet is found here intruding the hypersthene-gabbro. This is probably a marginal extension of the granophyric quartz-dolerite which outcrops further west.

Loc. 12 [457639]. Return to the south-west side of Stacan Dubha and then head westwards, along the contour to the south slope of Beinn na Seilg. Ascend Beinn na Seilg noting that the outcrops *en route* show the presence of a complex contact between the hypersthene-gabbro and the granophyric quartz-dolerite. On the higher part of the mountain this contact is flat-lying, the hypersthene-gabbro clearly forming a capping. Southwards too, the sinuosity of the contact and the occurrence of isolated patches of gabbro surrounded by granophyric dolerite show that the hypersthene-gabbro overlies the granophyric dolerite but their contact here must dip southwards at about the same general angle as the topographic slope. Individual contacts, where visible, however, dip both to the north and the south, the northerly dip possibly being produced by the attitude of the layering in the hypersthene-gabbro controlling marginal off-shoots from the upper surface of the granophyric dolerite. Both intrusions are cut by cone-sheets of the inner suite of Centre 2.

Loc. 13 [457642]. Cross the summit ridge of Beinn na Seilg between the cairns and ascend the western summit. A magnificent view is afforded of the Inner Hebridean islands, with the Outer Hebrides being visible on a clear day.

Loc. 14 [457643]. Descend from the summit ridge to an area of level ground lying north of the western summit. At this point the quartz-gabbro of Beinn na Seilg shows evidence that an olivine-gabbro of eucritic affinities has been profoundly affected by the later intrusion of a granophyric magma, resulting in the production of a quartz-feldspar mesostasis and alteration of the olivine and pyroxene. The granophyric component contains small apatite crystals. The boundary with the granophyric quartz-dolerite appears to dip steeply.

G

Loc. 15 [456645]. Continue northwards to the floor of the col separating the western and northern summits and cross to the western flank of the the mountain. The eucrite of Beinn nan Ord, which outcrops as distinctive ice-rounded, rusty-brown masses, has steeply dipping contacts with both the quartz-gabbros of Beinn na Seilg and Garbh-dhail. A view north-westwards to Beinn nan Ord shows the eucrite clearly extending up through 100 m or so of altitude. The northern summit of Beinn na Seilg is formed by a dyke-like arm of eucrite, with a near-vertical lateral contact against the quartz-gabbro of Garbh-dhail seen just north of the point where the arm leaves the main mass. More or less unbroken outcrops in this area show the arm to be continuous with the ring dyke. Near its contact with the eucrite, the quartz-gabbro of Garbh-dhail becomes rather fine-grained, more basic and brecciated.

Loc. 16 [457649]. Return to the col and follow the eastern flank of the northern summit ridge northwards. Here the quartz-gabbro of Garbh-dhail, cut by members of the inner cone-sheet suite of Centre 2 and the arm of eucrite, forms the roof of the quartz-gabbro of Faskadale (Centre 3). The edge of this younger intrusion is marked by a metamorphic zone in the older rocks, which forms a positive topographic feature that extends down the hillside. The top of the intrusion, immediately below this roof, is composed of granophyre, but further downhill the granophyre becomes more basic and grades into a rather acid quartz-gabbro which, in turn, passes into normal quartz-gabbro.

Loc. 17 [454647]. From below the eucrite crags of the northern summit ridge of Beinn na Seilg head south-westwards toward the marked fault-controlled valley of Struthan Bhraigh nam Allt which extends north-south along the west flank of the mountain. In the gorge cut by this stream, steeply dipping porphyritic dolerite cone-sheets cut the quartz-gabbro of Garbh-dhail. Xenoliths of fine-grained basic rock occur in the quartz-gabbro, and acid veins traverse both the xenoliths and the gabbro. These veins also cut the cone-sheets. Locally, the quartz-gabbro passes into olivine-bearing gabbro.

Loc. 18 [452654]. Follow the valley north for about 500 m to a peat-filled loch basin and then turn north-west for a further 200 m to the hillside on the north-east margin of Garbh-dhail. This hillside forms the southern end of a craggy north-south ridge which lies to the west of Struthan Bhraigh nam Allt. In this area a steep junction between the quartz-gabbro of Garbh-dhail and the older gabbro of Lochan an Aodainn is visible, the quartz-gabbro showing marginal chilling. The older gabbro is characterised by a distinctive black or bluish-black colour on weathered faces, which results from the presence of dark, clouded feldspars. Although the rock has the composition of an olivine-gabbro it often shows coarsely crystalline spots of acid material and granophyre veins. It also contains xenoliths of fine-grained material of quartz-dolerite affinities which in places form sheet-like bands. Looking south to the northern summit of Beinn na Seilg, the arm of eucrite can be clearly seen cutting through the quartz-gabbro of Garbh-dhail with a vertical contact.

Loc. 19 [452656]. Continue northwards along the ridge until basalt forming the inner margin of the older gabbro is found. To the east the basalt gives way to agglomerate, the fragments in which are similar to those in the vents of Centre 1, and consist of basalt, trachyte, tuff and quartz-dolerite. All fragments in the agglomerate show the effects of thermal alteration brought about by the adjacent plutonic intrusions. The basalt is similarly metamorphosed, but retains its major structures.

Loc. 20 [451658]. Return to the summit of the ridge and continue north to the crags at its termination, where a small felsite intrusion outcrops. It is a dark-grey, non-porphyritic rock, which on its eastern flank cuts the quartz-gabbro of Aodann. Although younger than the plutonic intrusions which are close by, the rock shows signs of thermal alteration, possibly indicating the presence of the Faskadale quartz-gabbro at no great depth below surface. The quartz-gabbro of Aodann, which occurs near the contact, is relatively fine-grained, but contains porphyritic feldspar crystals up to 5 mm long.

Loc. 21 [457663]. Head eastwards to cross the Struthan Bhraigh nam Allt, and a parallel stream about 100 m further east, and then turn north to the craggy hill that separates Lochan an Aodainn (a loch with a beautiful crescent of waterlilies) from Aodann. In this area the quartz-gabbro of Aodann exhibits an extremely variable texture and composition. A fine-grained facies forms the capping of the hill, but downhill a coarse-grained variety is found. An abrupt change between the two types occurs on the northern and southern slopes of the hill, but on the west the change appears gradational. Two separate phases of emplacement may be present, the fine-grained facies representing the earlier injection. Also, about 250 m east of Aodann at the contact between the coarse and fine-grained types, a finely crystalline dark-grey rock, banded with coarser lighter coloured material, is found, which may represent the remains of an even earlier, more basic, phase of intrusion. Occasionally within the gabbro xenolithic strips occur, with patches of fine-grained rock of quartz-dolerite affinities.

Loc. 22 [459663]. From the summit of the hill head eastwards to a point about 75 m south-west of the Kilchoan-Lighthouse road and 500 m east of Aodann. Here the outer margin of the quartz-gabbro of Aodann forms a rocky feature extending westwards somewhat obliquely to the hillside. Lying topographically below this feature, the

Great Eucrite of Centre 3 is seen displaying a typical coarse-grained appearance. Along the contact between these two rock types occurs a fine-grained porphyritic quartz-gabbro. This may represent either another facies of the Aodann quartz-gabbro or an early phase of the Great Eucrite. The junction with the Great Eucrite dips at about 70° to the south-west.

EXCURSION 3: Portuairk, Lighthouse and Achosnich

During the course of this excursion the plutonic intrusions of Centre 2 may be examined at the northern part of their outcrop, together with their relationships with the inner cone-sheet suite of Centre 2. Fluxion gabbro, the Great Eucrite of Centre 3, and the Beinn nan Ord eucrite, are visible at Portuairk, and the hypersthene-gabbro and granophyric quartz-dolerite between Eilean Carrach and Ardnamurchan Point. South of the road from Grigadale to Achosnich, the relationships between the Grigadale granophyre, the quartz-gabbro of Garbh-dhail and the older gabbro of Lochan an Aodainn are displayed. The best exposures of the granophyric quartz-dolerite, showing the effects of comagmatic acid and basic material, occur below high water mark near Eilean Carrach. This part of the excursion therefore requires a low tide. All other coastal localities, while best seen at low water, are accessible at most states of the tide.

Total distance (Portuairk-Portuairk) about 15 km, some of which is by vehicle.

Section A

From Kilchoan follow the Lighthouse road to Achosnich. Thence continue straight on for Portuairk, parking vehicles on the right of the road immediately before descending the steep hill into the village.

Loc. 1 [440682]. Gain access to the beach by following the stream down from the road bridge at the foot of the hill. The fluxion gabbro of Portuairk is well exposed along the coast, with its characteristic fluxion structure developed almost everywhere. Numerous bands of fine-grained rock are also present in the gabbro. An apparent contact of the fluxion gabbro with the Great Eucrite of Centre 3 occurs at high water mark at the head of a small sandy bay (due north of the Post Office), which is the mouth of the Allt Inbhir Luachair; but as the Great Eucrite in this area also shows fluxion structure it is difficult to distinguish the two. Near the Great Eucrite, vertical west-north-west joints are conspicuous in the fluxion gabbro. Acid veins containing angular and rounded blocks of fine-grained basic rock also occur. No clear contact with the eucrite of Beinn nan Ord is visible.

Loc. 2 [435684]. Following the coast westwards, the eucrite of Beinn nan Ord is exposed around the small headland north of the western end of the road at Portuairk. The rock here is an augite-rich variety, the augite forming large ophitic plates, essentially similar to the cognate xenoliths that occur in the allivalitic eucrite seen at locality 17. Olivine is fairly abundant, although acidified gabbro or eucrite also seems to be part of the intrusion. Xenolithic material in regular-running bands is prevalent. The eucrite is traversed by acid veins, the largest of which contains fragments of fine-grained basic rock.

Loc. 3 [434686]. Continue north-westwards, crossing a small rocky bay, for about 200 m along the coast, to another small headland. Continuous rock exposure in this area reveals a vague junction between the eucrite of Beinn nan Ord and quartz-gabbro of Loch Caorach. The relative age of these intrusions is not clear, although the two rocks are of contrasting type. The quartz-gabbro is a moderately coarse-grained rock containing pseudomorphs of olivine in magnetite and talc, which are associated with hypersthene. There is an abundant acid mesostasis.

Loc. 4 [425681]. From the headland return to the rocky bay, and thence climb westwards to the foot of the crags below the coast guard lookout station. Follow the crags westwards for about 200 m, crossing over the granophyric quartz-dolerite, until a marked north-south gully is reached. Turn south and follow the east side of the gully to its termination, and thence west, past a ruined croft, crossing hypersthene-gabbro, to the sandy beach which separates Eilean Carrach from the mainland (see coloured map). At the northern end of Eilean Carrach, mineralogical layering in the hypersthene-gabbro is seen to dip to the east at about 30°. Further south, on the island, xenolithic sheets in the hypersthene-gabbro also dip at about 30° to the east.

Loc. 5 [427680]. From the southern end of Eilean Carrach, cross the sandy beach to the east to the crags on the mainland adjacent to the beach. At the southern end of these crags, a westerly dipping granophyre sheet is found cutting the hypersthene-gabbro. This is an outlying intrusion of the granophyric component of the granophyric quartz-dolerite. The gabbro above the sheet is riddled with acid veins to a distance of 3 m or more, and continuity between these and the main sheet can be clearly established. The granophyre sheet contains numerous basic xenoliths similar to those found at locality 6G (below). Less altered and more angular fragments of hypersthene-gabbro are also present. Cone-sheets are observed cutting the hypersthene-gabbro in this area.

Loc. 6 [427679-424674]. On the mainland shore south of Eilean Carrach, the relationships between aphyric dolerite, porphyritic dolerite and granophyre, within the granophyric

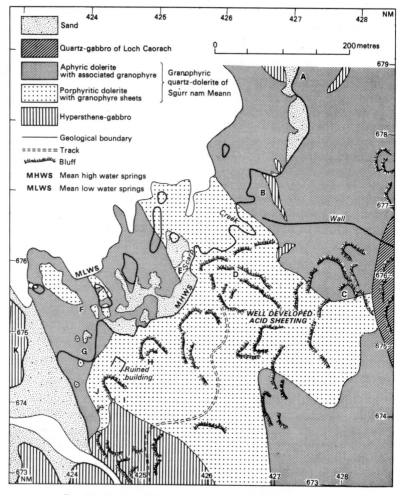

FIG. 13. Geology of the shore section south of Eilean Carrach
(based on Skelhorn and Elwell 1966).

94

quartz-dolerite, and those between the granophyric quartz-dolerite and the hypersthene-gabbro, are very well displayed. Grid references for the various sub-localities are not given, their positions being shown in Figure 13.

A. A steeply dipping contact between aphyric dolerite and hypersthene-gabbro is seen.

B. Aphyric dolerite is exposed containing inclusions of hypersthene-gabbro.

C. In this area the porphyritic dolerite in part overlies a complex association of aphyric dolerite and granophyre, but elsewhere their contact is steeply dipping, suggesting that the aphyric dolerite and granophyre complex consists of a series of sheeted intrusions, with frequent vertical linkage isolating lenticular bodies of the porphyritic dolerite host.

D. A sheet of flat-lying granophyre containing few inclusions of basic rock cuts the porphyritic dolerite. The porphyritic dolerite shows a fine-grained margin only a few centimetres wide.

E. Small-scale granophyric net-veining occurs in both aphyric and porphyritic dolerites and connects with large-scale sheets of granophyre containing a varied assemblage of basic inclusions.

F. The granophyre contains large inclusions of aphyric dolerite. The aphyric dolerite inclusions show rounded, fine-grained margins in some parts, and angular, coarse-grained margins in others.

G. Granophyric veins occur, isolating more or less rounded masses of aphyric dolerite which range from a metre or so up to more than 10 m across. The granophyric material is crowded with angular inclusions of basic rock. While these angular inclusions are of uniform texture throughout, the larger, rounded masses show a fine grained margin which may extend to 1 m or more in width, with a zone about 0.3 mm wide of dense rock rich in iron oxide immediately against the contact.

Within the fine-grained margins a faint banded structure is usually present, and in some places a parallel development of minute feldspathic veinlets is seen.

H. Porphyritic dolerite is cut by sheets of granophyre in which inclusions of basic rock occur. Individual sheets are not very persistent, but dyke-like apophyses which link the sheets at different levels are numerous. The sheets are either flat-lying or have a gentle westerly dip.

I. A steeply dipping contact between porphyritic dolerite and hypersthene-gabbro can be seen in this area.

J. Porphyritic dolerite is here cut by granophyre. The dolerite does not have a fine-grained margin and the contact truncates the phenocrysts in the dolerite. Aphyric dolerite inclusions within the granophyre occasionally form contacts with the porphyritic dolerite and, in some places, joint-bounded blocks of porphyritic dolerite have subsided into the aphyric dolerite.

K. In this general area the hypersthene-gabbro shows the development of a mineralogical layering, the layering dipping east at about 15°. Layered sections of the gabbro are separated both vertically and laterally by non-layered gabbro.

Loc. 7 [415674]. Pass through the caravan site east of Port na Carraidh, and thence along a track which joins the Lighthouse road by the bridge across the Allt Grigadale. Follow the road westwards to the Lighthouse at Ardna-murchan Point (the most westerly point on the British main-land). On the shore west of the Lighthouse is exposed the quartz-dolerite outer marginal facies of the hypersthene-gabbro. Eastwards the rock passes into quartz-gabbro, which here represents a rather acid facies of the hypersthene-gabbro. The rock is cut by steeply dipping porphyritic and non-porphyritic cone-sheets of Centre 2, and also by basic dykes.

Loc. 8 [417667]. Return south-east along the Lighthouse road until easy crossing of the Allt a Bhriaghlann is afforded, and thence south-west to the rocks north of a conspicuous area of wind-blown sand, forming the southern shore of the bay south of the Lighthouse (Bhriaghlann). At this point, away from the marginal facies of the hypersthene-gabbro, xenoliths of basic hornfels are seen dipping east at moderate angles. The gabbro texture is very variable and the xenoliths are sometimes surrounded by a coarse gabbro which is more feldspathic, and has less iron ore, than the normal facies.

Loc. 9 [426667]. Head east across country for about 700 m, passing two small cairns, to a point on the Allt a Bhriaghlann, about 300 m south of the road, where a wooden bridge allows access to a series of rocky outcrops. These show layering in the hypersthene-gabbro dipping east at about 25°.

Loc. 10 [427672]. Return across the wooden bridge and head north to regain the Lighthouse road. Continue east along the road to a point about 250 m beyond the bridge across the Allt Grigadale. The quartz-gabbro of Loch Caorach is exposed on the roadside, and about 100 m north of the road a contact with the granophyric quartz-dolerite is found. Close to this contact the quartz-gabbro becomes finer in texture, and is cut by veins of gabbro-aplite and augite-rich gabbro-pegmatite, which run parallel to the contact. At the contact the fine-grained gabbro becomes porphyritic and resembles the adjoining porphyritic dolerite.

Loc. 11 [435669]. Continue east along the Lighthouse road to an area about 300 m beyond Grigadale, where the younger quartz-gabbro of Beinn Bhuidhe is exposed in several roadside positions. Between these, a considerable variation in the degree of development of an acid mesostasis is present. In the most unaffected state the rock is a moderately coarse, ophitic dolerite, but the effect of the later acid migration brings about an albitization of the feldspars and a recrystallisation of the pyroxene.

Section B

If proceeding directly to this section of the excursion from Kilchoan, vehicles may be parked on the left of the road about 100 m towards the Lighthouse from Achosnich. Lying mostly to the south of the Achosnich-Lighthouse road, the Grigadale granophyre presents a series of interesting relationships with the surrounding intrusions. These indicate that the quartz-gabbro of Garbh-dhail has been intruded in two phases, separated by the emplacement of the granophyre. The geology of the area is shown in Figure 14.

Loc. 12 [441669]. East of Grigadale, the Lighthouse-Achosnich road crosses a low peat-filled basin. As the road rises further east on to higher ground, however, a contact between the Grigadale granophyre and the older quartz-gabbro of Beinn Bhuidhe is exposed just a few metres north of the road. The contact can be traced for a short distance and appears to run east-west. The granophyre is fine-grained at the contact, whereas the gabbro is coarse-grained. The gabbro is also cut by a series of granophyre veins which range from 1 cm to 5 cm or so in width. Most of these veins run parallel to the contact and have direct cross connections with the main granophyre.

Loc. 13 [442668]. Follow the edge of the ridge of high ground to the south to some crags which lie about 150 m south-east of the road. Here the granophyre has several well-exposed contacts with the older gabbro of Lochan an Aodainn. The contacts are sharp and nearly vertical and the granophyre has developed a fine-grained chilled margin. Acid veins in the gabbro are numerous and increase in

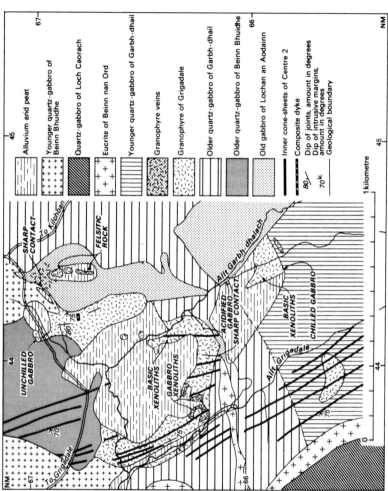

Alluvium and peat

Younger quartz-gabbro of Beinn Bhuidhe

Quartz-gabbro of Loch Caorach

Eucrite of Beinn nan Ord

Younger quartz-gabbro of Garbh-dhail

Granophyre veins

Granophyre of Grigadale

Older quartz-gabbro of Garbh-dhail

Older quartz-gabbro of Beinn Bhuidhe

Old gabbro of Lochan an Aodainn

Inner cone-sheets of Centre 2

Composite dyke

Dip of joints, amount in degrees
Dip of intrusive margins, amount in degrees
Geological boundary

1 kilometre

FIG. 14. Geology of the area east of Grigadale, Centre 2 (based on Paithankar 1968).

99

abundance towards the granophyre from which they originate. These veins vary between about 2 cm and 8 cm in thickness.

Loc. 14 [443668]. On the higher slopes of the ridge of ground, a tongue of granophyre cuts the Lochan an Aodainn gabbro, and masses of felsitic rock occur within the gabbro. The northern area of felsite is cut by a porphyritic cone-sheet of the inner suite of Centre 2. The felsites are probably associated with the granophyre.

Loc. 15 [444658]. Continue south along the ridge of high ground to the Allt Garbh-dhalach. Cross this stream and follow its west bank upstream until an important tributary enters from the south. Thence follow the west bank of the tributary for about 250 m upstream before heading west for a further 100 m to a series of outcrops which lie to the south of an extensive area of peat. Coarse-grained granophyre is found there in sharp contact with the quartz-gabbro of Garbh-dhail, which is chilled against the granophyre. This quartz-gabbro is therefore a member of the younger intrusive phase.

Loc. 16 [440662]. Return along the west bank of the Allt Garbh-dhalach to the ridge of high ground which had been followed south from the Lighthouse road, and continue along this ridge to the south-west for about 250 m. A sharp junction can be observed at this point on a flat rock surface between the granophyre and the quartz-gabbro of Garbh-dhail. A marginal, fine-grained facies of quartz-gabbro is in contact with fine-grained granophyre, but a metre or so away from the contact the granophyre is medium-grained and contains basic inclusions. This suggests that the granophyre is younger than the quartz-gabbro, which must be a member of the older intrusive phase.

Loc. 17 [439661]. About 150 m further south-west, the characteristic rusty-brown, ice-rounded masses of the Beinn nan Ord eucrite are reached. These exposures are part of an easterly projection of eucrite which cuts across the quartz-gabbro of Garbh-dhail. The eucrite is allivalitic in character and contains small, rounded masses of coarsely ophitic augite-rich eucrite which may be cognate xenoliths.

Loc. 18 [438663]. Keeping to the higher ground, follow the east bank of the Allt Grigadale for about 250 m to the north, where large masses of gabbro occur as isolated exposures within a general area of granophyre. Although separated from each other by peat, they are probably parts of one large gabbro xenolith. The westernmost area of gabbro is profusely invaded by granophyre veins. The road to Achosnich is best reached by returning east along the high ground, and thence down the west bank of the Allt Garbh-dhalach to a wooden bridge which lies a short distance south of the road.

EXCURSION 4: Sanna Bay to Rubha Carrach

This short excursion allows an examination of the granophyric quartz-dolerite, hypersthene-gabbro and outer cone-sheets of Centre 2, an agglomerate related to Centre 1, and the gabbro of Plocaig (Centre 3). Along the coast between Sanna Bay and Sanna Point a series of sills of granophyric quartz-dolerite can be seen cutting the hypersthene-gabbro. Also in this area the best examples of mineralogical layering in the hypersthene-gabbro intrusion are seen. On the north coast, east of Rubha an Duin Bhain, the hypersthene-gabbro contains occasional acid xenoliths and at its contact with the M. Liassic sandstone an interesting pseudo-beccia is developed. From the Glendrian Caves to Rubha Carrach the magnificent sea cliff shows tuffs and coarse agglomerate. Low tide is advisable for this excursion.

Total distance (Sanna-Sanna) about 7 km.

From Kilchoan follow the road to Sanna. At Sanna Bay vehicles may be parked just beyond the telephone kiosk. Follow the footpath inland of the sand dunes northwards to the footbridge across the Allt Sanna immediately upstream from Burnbank. (This is a private bridge which may be used by the public. Users, however, are requested to make a contribution for aid to the handicapped, in the box provided on the bridge.) Proceed down the north bank of the stream to the shore.

Loc. 1 [443697]. Below high water mark alongside the Allt Sanna a series of exposures show granophyre containing inclusions of both aphyric and porphyritic dolerite and hypersthene-gabbro. The inclusions of aphyric dolerite occasionally show the development of a dark margin against the granophyre. At its northern limit, the granophyric quartz-dolerite can be seen to dip steeply northwards beneath the hypersthene-gabbro.

Loc. 2 [441699]. Continue along the coast westwards for about 300 m and then northwards for about 150 m, across the root of a small peninsula, to a sandy bay where exposures of a sill of granophyric quartz-dolerite are again present.

Loc. 3 [441700]. In the area about 100 m north of the sandy bay, the hypersthene-gabbro shows the best examples of perfectly developed mineralogical layering in the intrusion. The layers, which dip south at angles between 10° and 20°, are formed by variation in the proportion of those minerals normally found in the rock, namely plagioclase feldspar, augite, hypersthene, olivine and magnetite. Although the compositional variation is usually slight, occasional bands of anorthosite, peridotite and iron ore are found. Slight textural changes accompany the mineralogical variations, and a degree of preferred orientation of the feldspar crystals is usually developed parallel to the layering, which is best seen where the layering is more steeply inclined. Although the sequence of layers is usually haphazard, a succession occasionally develops comprising a lower group containing distinctive clustered aggregates of olivine (giving a curious pock-marked appearance to the weathered rock), and an upper group which is characterised by the presence of rather shattered plagioclase phenocrysts. In some places rhythmic banding, produced by variation of the feldspar/pyroxene ratio, is also present. Some olivine-rich bands afford textural evidence for gravity accumulation of the olivine.

Loc. 4 [441704]. Continue northwards across hypersthene-gabbro with a sporadic development of fine net-veining by granophyre and containing the occasional rounded xenolith, to the wave-cut platform on the coast about 200 m north of the cairn marking the high ground of Sanna Point. At this point a sub-horizontal sill of granophyre with aphyric dolerite, about 1 m thick, cuts the hypersthene-gabbro.

Loc. 5 [449703]. Regain the top of the cliffs and follow the coast eastwards for about 800 m to the fort of Duin Bhain and thence to the sandy bay about 150 m south-east of the fort. The boundary between the hypersthene-gabbro and a cone-sheet complex passes roughly east to west through this bay. To the north is the high ground of Duin Bhain, in which individual cone-sheets prove difficult to recognise, but occasional bands of Jurassic sandstone within the complex allow the recognition of a number of discrete intrusions. Separating this complex from the marginal quartz-dolerite facies of the hypersthene-gabbro is a granophyre sheet containing crystals of plagioclase feldspar and augite in a matrix of micrographic quartz and feldspar. To the south of the bay the marginal facies passes into normal hypersthene-gabbro.

Loc. 6 [451702]. Follow the coast eastwards, keeping below high water mark, for about 200 m, where occasional

H

rounded masses, up to about 10 cm in diameter, of acid material occur within the hypersthene-gabbro. These may represent xenolithic blocks of Jurassic sandstone.

Loc. 7 [453700]. Continue south-eastwards along the coast to the rocky bay north of Plocaig. On the west side of the bay, to the south of a small high water island, the hypersthene-gabbro is invaded by a mass of granophyre which net-veins the gabbro. The mass has inclusions of fine-grained basic rock and appears to be both cut by and cutting a steeply dipping sheet of similarly fine-grained basic rock. Although having an east-west outcrop the granophyre is difficult to trace westwards, but on the east side of the bay, slightly to the north of its projected strike position, the granophyre displays a sheeted form about 2 m thick dipping to the south at about 40° and extensively net-veining the overlying hypersthene-gabbro. The granophyre is composed of crystals of zoned plagioclase feldspar (labradorite to oligoclase) and augite, in a matrix of quartz and alkali feldspar showing some micrographic texture. This intrusion may represent a unique acid cone-sheet of the Centre 2 suite, but, more probably, is related to the granophyric quartz-dolerite sills which outcrop within the hypersthene-gabbro further to the west.

Loc. 8 [460703] Follow the outcrop of the granophyre sheet eastwards for about 400 m to a sandy bay (beware of areas of quicksand), and then north-eastwards across the dark-coloured hypersthene-gabbro for a further 300 m to the lighter-coloured quartz-bearing marginal facies of the gabbro. The actual margin of the intrusion trends north-west to south-east across the shore. In this immediate area the character of the margin is intrusive, but this gives way inland to fault-controlled contact. Interesting acid xenoliths, probably of Jurassic sandstone, have been recorded as occurring within the gabbro about 5 m from the contact just above high water mark. Of even more interest, however, is the presence of a curious "breccia", best seen below high water mark, immediately outside the gabbro boundary. The rock consists of light-coloured angular fragments up to a few centimetres in length, composed of sutured quartz grains which are invaded by irregular veinlets of feldspar and quartz, set in a fine-grained matrix which is also light coloured. The amount of feldspathic material in the fragments increases towards their margins and the "breccia" is considered to have resulted by feldspathization of the Jurassic sandstone host. The breaking up of some fragments and the occasional development of chlorite around the fragments has been attributed to mobilisation.

Loc. 9 [461705]. Continue north-eastwards along the shore, crossing M. Liassic sandstone cut both by numerous cone-sheets of the outer suite of Centre 2 and by olivine-bearing basic dykes, to Glendrian Caves. The seacliff forming the western shore of Rubha Carrach is composed of coarse agglomerate and tuff. In addition to fragments of Mesozoic sediments and basaltic lava, these volcanics contain some acid material, suggesting that the vent explosions may be associated with the formation of an acid magma. The agglomerates and tuffs are cut by the cone-sheets and the basic dykes.

Loc. 10 [455698]. Return south-westwards along the shore to the sandy bay. Continue along the cliff top westwards for about 150 m until a marked north-south gully is reached. Follow the top of the gully southwards to its termination and thence for about a further 250 m alongside a north-south artificial dyke to an isolated rocky outcrop which lies about 250 m east of Plocaig. Here the gabbro of Plocaig is exposed. This small, elongate mass extends for a short distance between the hypersthene-gabbro and the Great Eucrite, and appears to be a distinct intrusion from both its neighbours. It is a coarse olivine-gabbro containing xenoliths of hypersthene-gabbro, generally considered to be related to Centre 3.

EXCURSION 5: Ben (or Beinn) Hiant

The purpose of this excursion is to examine the Tertiary and pre-Tertiary rocks of Centre 1 on the east side of Ben Hiant. Semi-pelitic Moine rocks are first observed overlain by badly exposed Mesozoic sediments, all these rocks being extensively cut by various types of Tertiary dykes.

The basal Tertiary plateau basalts are observed overlying the sedimentary rocks and also an igneous agglomerate infilling an early vent on Ben Hiant. Finally, some of the other Centre 1 rocks are examined, particularly andesitic pitchstone lavas, porphyritic and non-porphyritic dolerites and a small outcrop of trachyte.

Total distance (Kilchoan-Kilchoan) about 26 km by vehicle: 4 km walking (very steep and hard in places).

Cars may be parked in the road cutting on the south bank of a stream 0.4 miles ($\frac{1}{2}$ km+) south of the 13-mile post from Salen (*room for two cars only*).

[552635-548635]. Stream section examined during a traverse up the largest of three streams, that is the one beside the cutting. Figure 3 shows this area in detail.

No exposures occur between the road and 100 m or so upstream. Always walk as close to the stream as possible. The first exposures, occurring just below a small silver birch tree in the stream, are typical Moine rocks comprising pale-coloured quartzites (or psammites) with micaceous bands. At this point a large dolerite dyke crosses the stream, cutting the Moines, and its contact is clearly visible in a small waterfall below the tree. Upstream a series of dolerite dykes is observed with occasional igneous/igneous contacts in the bed of the stream. These dykes continue upstream for another 60 m until Moine rocks are observed once more. At this point the river banks are more gentle and just enough Moine rocks occur to estimate their strike as north-west to south-east and their dip as 30° to the south-west.

Two silver birch trees form an arch over the stream and here the Moine rocks show well-developed micaceous planes, dipping to the south-west at variable angles of between 20° and 35°. Further upstream, the rocks become more highly coloured, where three huge boulders occur. Several small dykes cut across the stream at this point, two of which are clearly seen on the north bank of the river. Above this point a major waterfall occurs, more than 6 m high, with another waterfall just above it. The rocks here are still Moines, but quite altered from Moine rocks further downstream in that they are fissile and often strongly coloured, dipping south-west to south-south-west at angles of up to 40°.

Above the second waterfall the ground flattens out and is grassy. Immediately above this occasional exposures of Triassic sediments of variable thickness (0.3 m) can be seen in the stream bed. In this section of ground the L. Lias first occurs where the ground becomes boggy and, although exposures are rare, rock occurs about 20 m downstream from the foot of the steep valley (below the confluence of two small streams). A carbonated dyke cuts across the first stream and the boundary with the Tertiary plateau basalts is reached just below the confluence. Between the first basalts Richey et al. (1930) recorded occasional exposures of basal Tertiary muds but these can no longer be observed here.

The plateau basalts here are thin and composed of an alkali-olivine type being best observed in the southern stream channel. The ridge separating the two stream channels from each other is controlled by a large east-west trending dyke which may be a multiple intrusion. Further upstream along the southern channel a series of knolls are reached on the south bank of the stream. At this point the east-west dyke on the ridge shows excellent variation features, especially a "brecciated" central section. A well-defined contact between basalts (below) and highly brecciated agglomerates (above) on the south bank of the stream channel should be noted, the contact of the vent wall dipping to the south-west at 20°, this contact occurring about 5 m above the stream bed. Above this point a large brown bluff on the south bank of the stream marks a dyke intruding the agglomerate. The river gradient now increases and the stream banks are steep. Climb up, examining agglomerate which becomes fresher and less brecciated, until the lip of the scarp is reached at the last waterfall. Continue upstream until a well-defined and easily observed north-east to south-west trending cone-sheet crosses the stream, shown on coloured map at [547635].

Go south-west from this point for about 1 km climbing over undulating and boggy ground until the final rock face leading to the summit is directly above [537629]. A gully trending north-west to south-east cuts upwards through these crags, and at the bottom of the southern line of crags (separated from the main rock face) good examples of porphyritic dolerite with large feldspar crystals and with occasional dolerite xenoliths occur. Behind this line of crags the main Ben Hiant dolerites are seen and one can climb up or collect from scree boulders fallen down. On a fine day Ben Hiant should be climbed both for the view to the south, where the major plateau basalts can be seen on the north coast of Mull, and the general view of the region including the Sound of Mull and Morvern. On the way up the dolerites can be examined in more detail (see p. 22). Return to the porphyritic dolerite and go south-eastwards to [542628], where pitchstone lavas occur as a hump at the south end of main slopes overlooking the old abandoned village of Bourblaige (see coloured map). Two or three individual flows may be recognised because of the vesicular character of the top of each flow and the dip of the boundary between the flows can be measured.

After examination of all the rocks in this area return to the road, examining spheroidal weathering basalts well exposed in stream sections on the way. Return to vehicle and then go to 12-mile post from Salen and just north of bridge over the river Allt Tòrr na Mòine at [555627], where a line of crags on the west side of the road marks a small flow of trachyte — the only observed rock of this type in the region.

During the course of the excursion to Ben Hiant it is possible that a herd of deer will be observed, particularly in the valley which runs south-westwards from the bottom of the Ben Hiant summit.

EXCURSION 6: The augite-diorite of Camphouse, and Faskadale Bay.

Section A

The excursion examines a small intrusion with spectacular mineralogy situated about 3 km from Kilchoan and involving about 2 km of walking over boggy ground with some streams to cross. Excellent views of the western side of Ben Hiant are also seen during the walk.

Cars should be parked at [511642] just before the bend on the main Kilchoan-Salen road. At this road bend is a concrete pit for silage storage and the track runs from there down to a bridge crossing the Allt Choire Mhuilinn stream. Below the bridge Moine schists are found with frequent cross-cutting cone-sheets, the latter exhibiting chilled margins. The track bends north and goes round a field with occasional knolls marking the sites of cone-sheets. Thereafter a series of sheep pens is reached and the track bends round these until at the far side it divides, the northern branch being taken. The track runs over limestones of Lower Jurassic age (Broadford Beds) often preserved in the vicinity of cone-sheets where baking has occurred. Finally, the track is crossed by a deer fence with a gate in it. The augite-diorite "boss" occurs about 100 m north of this gate on the west side of the fence being marked by about ten isolated small exposures of black rock. Inspection shows variable grain size from coarse to pegmatitic with augites occasionally visible some 10-20 mm long. Although the form of the intrusion is difficult to ascertain, it appears dome-shaped from the local topography, but its age relationships with the Centre 1 intrusions are unknown.

Section B

The object of this excursion is to examine rock types of Centre 1 in north Ardnamurchan which were not seen in the Ben Hiant excursion, particularly vent agglomerates with plentiful xenoliths, gabbros and granophyres.

Total distance (Kilchoan-Kilchoan) 31 km, of which only 2 km are by foot.

About 7 km eastwards from Kilchoan, the north (left-hand) fork of the road is taken to Faskadale (and Achateny) and about 3 to 4 km along this north road the left-hand fork is again taken to Faskadale. Cars are parked on flat land just before farm buildings at [501707]. Low tide is preferred for this section, which is shown in Fig. 15a.

Loc. 1 [498707]. The track leads westwards from the farm at Faskadale to the pebble beach which is crossed towards the mouth of the Allt Faskadale stream, which enters Faskadale Bay about 250 m from Faskadale farm. The shallow Allt Faskadale can usually be crossed here fairly easily (although a small footbridge occurs about 150 m upstream), and the outcrop of rocks examined. These

110

represent a sheet of basic rocks dipping to the north-east at 30°. From the coloured map the major north-south trending (Allt Faskadale) fault enters Faskadale Bay here, and it may be that these rocks represent a cone-sheet which has had its attitude disturbed by this fault.

Loc. 2 [498708]. From the mouth of the Allt Faskadale the shoreline of Faskadale Bay is followed round to the west and north until a large shelf of agglomerate, well displayed at low tide, is reached. The agglomerate is considered to be an early intrusion of Centre 1 age and contains angular fragments of Moine schists, spherulitic rhyolites and dacites, basic dolerites and lava flows. It is of importance to note that no rhyolite or dacite lavas have been observed in Ardnamurchan, so that these fragments either represent parts of a totally eroded acid lava cover or pieces from an acid magma which crystallised in the original volcanic vent and which was disrupted at a time just prior to the formation of the vent agglomerates.

Within this agglomerate north-west to south-east trending cone-sheets (dipping south-west at 40°) and north-south trending vertical dykes are observed. Both of these narrow intrusive types are basic in composition.

Loc. 3 [497711]. Continue along the coast for about 300 m to the north-west and a vertical "wall" of quartz-gabbro representing the old gabbro west of Faskadale can be observed intruding the agglomerate. At this place the gabbro is about 20 m wide and has the appearance of a porphyritic dolerite. However, the porphyritic rock is usually a marginal facies developed particularly along the east-west northern edge of the quartz-gabbro and grades into normal quartz-gabbro to the south. The fine-grained porphyritic gabbro is chilled against the agglomerate and therefore post-dates the vent formation (and also post-dates all lava rock types found as inclusions in the agglomerate)

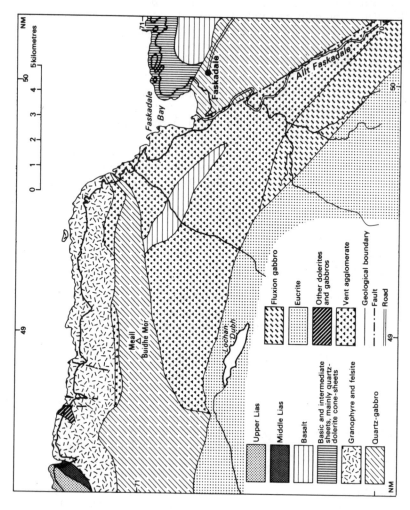

FIG. 15a. Geology of Faskadale Bay (after Richey, map 19). Minor intrusions removed.

Legend:

- Upper Lias
- Middle Lias
- Basalt
- Basic and intermediate sheets, mainly quartz-dolerite cone-sheets
- Granophyre and felsite
- Quartz-gabbro
- Fluxion gabbro
- Eucrite
- Other dolerites and gabbros
- Vent agglomerate
- Geological boundary
- Fault
- 49 Road

112

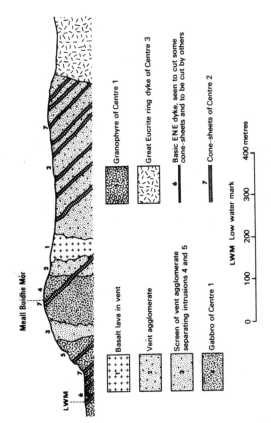

Fig. 15b. North-south section of rocks, west of Faskadale Bay (based on Richey et al. 1930).

Meall Buidhe Mòr

LWM

LWM Low water mark

0   100   200   300   400 metres

1 | Basalt lava in vent

2 | Vent agglomerate

3 | Screen of vent agglomerate separating intrusions 4 and 5

4 | Gabbro of Centre 1

5 | Granophyre of Centre 1

6 | Great Eucrite ring dyke of Centre 3

6 — Basic ENE dyke, seen to cut some cone-sheets and to be cut by others

7 ▬▬▬ Cone-sheets of Centre 2

113

but is earlier than the cone-sheets and dykes which cut this gabbro further inland. On the exposed quartz-gabbro rocks on the cliff top, glacial striae suggest an ice movement towards the west-north-west.

Loc. 4 [497711]. About 50 m along the coast, north-westwards from the northern gabbro/agglomerate contact, another contact is reached where a granophyre is intruded into the agglomerate. The contact is sharp and inclined southwards at a steep angle. Further inland a contact between granophyre and quartz-gabbro can be found at [491771] dipping to the south at 70°, and showing a chilled margin of granophyre against the quartz-gabbro. Thus the granophyre must represent the youngest of the three main intrusions examined on this trip and which are shown in section in Fig. 15b.

The granophyre is a typical non-porphyritic acid rock with alkali feldspar and quartz occurring in a micrographic structure.

Loc. 5 [491711]. If sufficient time is available follow the coast round to the west for about 500 m, until a black-weathering mass of ultrabasic rocks is found as a "screen" about 40 m wide. This black igneous rock is an olivine-gabbro which is locally peridotitic in composition. It separates the acid granophyre to the east from another, more basic granophyre to the west. This second granophyric type is characterised by the presence of green-brown elongate crystals of hornblende in the hand specimen. Both types of granophyre are altered by the basic olivine-gabbro screen.

Return to Faskadale along the cliff tops and observe Rhum, Muck, Eigg and Skye on a clear day. Sea birds such as shags, cormorants and gannets are commonly seen along this coast, and seals have been observed in the sea close to the shore in Faskadale Bay.

EXCURSION 7: Ring intrusions of Centre 3

The purpose of this excursion is to examine the more important ring intrusions ascribed to Centre 3 and the dramatic effect these rings have had on the topography of the area.

Take the road from Kilchoan to Sanna to the bridge across the stream Amhainn Chro Bheinn at the first sharp left bend beyond the junction with the Lighthouse road.

Loc. 1 [476650]. Just past the stream there are several roadside exposures where it is possible to examine the outer-most ring intrusion of Centre 3, the quartz-gabbro of Faskadale. Travel north from here through the wide ring intrusion of the Great Eucrite and park beside the road just to the west of Craig an Airgid (see coloured map).

Loc. 2 [472668]. To the east of the road on the western slopes of Craig an Airgid the exposure of eucrite is good and there is much evidence of ice action. The eucrite can be most easily separated from quartz-gabbro in hand specimen by having more plagioclase feldspar and less magnetite. The eucrite, which is extensively exposed and occupies higher ground, can often be distinguished by its weathering to almost "purplish" colour. From the summit of Craig an Airgid there is an excellent view across the complex of Centre 3 if visibility is good.

On the western side of the road (about 200 m from the road) is an excellent exposure of the quartz-dolerite veined with granophyre, forming a small knoll surrounded by boggy ground. There is also some net-veining of the dolerite by the granophyre. The very sharp contact between the dolerite and the later granophyre is very noticeable, but the granophyre lacks a chilled edge against the dolerite. Analyses of the dolerite and granophyre show no discernible change in chemistry of either rock type at the contact (Walsh 1971). This is despite the considerable difference in chemistry of the two rocks, the dolerite containing about 51% SiO_2 whereas the granophyre has about 72%. The dolerite veined with granophyre occurs as an incomplete ring intrusion and its exposure is intermittent.

Continue northwards along the road, crossing the biotite-eucrite, which is well exposed beside the road, although biotite cannot be detected in hand specimen (or in thin sections in most cases).

Loc. 3 [474674]. Further north there is parking space beside a new bridge which crosses the Allt Uamha na Muice stream (the section of stream which joins the Allt Màm a'Ghaill to the Allt Sanna). From this point a number of the intrusions of Centre 3 can be examined.

The stream cuts through the Sìthean Mór fluxion gabbro. The outer portion of this crescent-shaped mass seen in the stream section to the south east of the bridge is a quartz-gabbro, cut by a narrow acidified dyke. In the stream section to the north-west of the bridge the inner part of the Sìthean Mór intrusion can be examined. Near the stream fluxioning can be observed, which becomes progressively more important towards the inner margin of the intrusion. Fluxioning can also be seen in many exposures on the slopes of Sìthean Mór (to the west of the bridge). The marginal apophysis of the Sìthean Mór intrusion is seen on the southern slopes of Sìthean Mór.

Return to the stream Allt Uamha na Muice, continue up this to the north-west and examine the inner eucrite. This is quite indistinguishable in the field (or laboratory) from the Great Eucrite. Further upstream the quartz-gabbro can be observed, but although the exposure in the stream section is good, no sharp contacts between the various ring intrusions can be seen.

Loc. 4 [463683]. From Sìthean Mór travel along the road to Sanna and park at Achnaha. The road to Achnaha roughly follows the outcrop of the quartz-gabbro, and at a roadside cutting where the road crosses the tonalite the outer margin of the latter can be examined [466679].

From Achnaha it is convenient to walk into the very centre of the complex to examine the rocks attributed to the final phase in the formation of Centre 3; the distinctive intermediate rocks, the tonalite and quartz-monzonite. From a point just to the north of the houses at Achnaha traverse due east, climbing first over the higher ground which makes up the Glendrian fluxion gabbro. The fluxion structure is quite well seen here. Then cross on to the tonalite, which is poorly exposed in an area of lower-lying ground. However, travelling eastwards exposure improves and the distinctive features of the tonalite rock can be easily seen with its light colour and abundant large platy crystals of biotite. Finally, the quartz-monzonite is reached 800 m east of Achnaha, on rising ground, on which stands a small cairn.

When visibility is good the dramatic effect of the geology of Centre 3 on the topography of the area can be seen from this spot. The Great Eucrite forms a vast natural amphitheatre surrounding the lower-lying inner complex. Standing on the quartz-monzonite and looking due south, it is possible to see the peak of Creag an Airgid. To the east is the ridge which includes Meall Meadhoin, to the north-east is the peak of Meall an Fhìr-eoin (Eagle Hill), to the northwest is Meall Clach an Daraich, to the west Meall Sanna, and to the south-west Beinn na-h-Imeilte. Extensive ice-scoured outcrops of eucrite can be seen on all these peaks (see coloured map). In addition an inner ridge can be seen in the inner complex, formed by the Glendrian fluxion gabbro, extending from Druim Liath in the south round to above the old Glendrian farmhouse in the east and finally near to Achnaha. The quartz-gabbros in the centre usually occupy lower-lying land which has been previously cultivated.

An excellent view across Centre 3 can be obtained on a clear day from the peak of Meall an Fhìr-eoin.

APPENDIX

Glossary of Ardnamurchan place names
(translated by K. MacDonald)

An article on "Ardnamurchan Place-names", by Angus Henderson, appears in *The Celtic Review*, 1915, pp. 149-168.

Pronunciation

Initial Bh or Mh equals *V*, but after a broad vowel equals *W*, as in English "now".
Initial C equals *K*.
Initial Fh is silent.
Initial Ph equals *F*.
Initial Sh or Th equals *H*.
Initial S after An t- is silent.
Final — aidh equals *y* as in *my*.
Final — idh equals *y* as in *duty*.
Th final, or when flanked with vowels, is a strong breathing.
Ch in contact with *a*, *o* or *u* is a strong guttural as in *loch*.
Ch in contact with *e* or *i* is a guttural as in German *ich*.

Achnaha	: Field of the Kiln (Henderson translates "the field of the ford, the ford being on the rather large stream known as Allt Uamha na Muice". The difficulty here is that *àth*, "ford" is usually masculine, whereas *àth* in the above name is clearly feminine: hence my translation "kiln".)
Achosnich	: Field of Sighing
Allt Choire Mhuilinn	: Burn from the Corrie of the Mill
Allt Faskadale	: Burn of Faskadale (Norse: "ship-dale")

Allt Màm a' Ghaill	:	Burn of the Stranger's Hill
Allt Tòrr na Mòine	:	Peat-heap Burn
Amhainn Chrò Bheinn	:	River of Enclosure Mountain
An Acairseid	:	The Anchorage
Aodann	:	Face/Slope
Ardslignish	:	Headland of Shells
Beinn an Leathaid	:	Mountain of the Incline
Beinn Bhuidhe	:	Yellow Mountain
Beinn Hiant	:	Blessed Mountain
Beinn na h-Imeilte	:	Mountain of the Many Streams
Beinn na h-Urchrach	:	Mountain of the Shot
Beinn nan Losgann	:	Mountain of Toads
Beinn nan Ord	:	Mountain of the Hammers
Beinn na Seilg	:	Mountain of the Hunt
Camas nan Clacha Móra	:	Bay of Large Stones
Camas nan Ceall	:	Bay of (Monastic) Cells (alt. Bay of Pledges)
Craig an Airgid	:	Rock of Silver
Eilean Carrach	:	Rough Island
Eilean nan Seachd Seisrichean	:	Island of Seven Ploughteams
Garbh Dhail (-dhail)	:	Rough Meadow
Garbhlach Mhór	:	Large Rough Place
Garbh Rubha	:	Rough Point
Glas Eilean	:	Grey Island
Glen Drian	:	Glen of Briar
Kilchoan	:	Congan's Church
Lochan a' Mhadaidh Riabhaich	:	Little Loch of the Brindled Dog
Loch an Aodainn	:	Loch of the Slope
Lochan Dóbhrain	:	Little Loch of the Otter
Lochan na Crannaig	:	Little Loch of the Crannog
Loch Caorach	:	Loch of Sheep
Meall an Fhìr-eoin	:	Hill of the Eagle
Meall an Tarmachain	:	Hill of Ptarmigan

Meall Buidhe Mór	:	Large Yellow Hill
Meall Clach an Daraich	:	Hill of the Stone of the Oak
Meall Meadhoin	:	Middle Hill
Meall nan Con	:	Hill of the Dogs
Ormsaigbeg	:	Little Ormsaig (Norse: "serpent bay")
Port an Eilein Mhoir	:	Port of the Large Island
Port Bàn	:	White Port
Port Mìn	:	Smooth Port
Rubha a'Chait	:	Headland of the Cat (reading *Chait* and not *Choit*. There is a word *coit*, "boat", but it appears to be of the wrong gender.
Rubha Aird an Iasgaich	:	Point of Fishing Headland (reading *Iasgaich* and not *Lasgaich*, which seems to be a map misprint.)
Rubha a' Mhìle	:	Headland of the Mile
Rubha an Dùin Bhàin	:	Headland of the White Fort
Rubha Carrach	:	Rough Headland
Sgeir Fhada	:	Long Skerry
Sgeir Ghobhlach	:	Forked Skerry
Sgùrr nam Meann	:	Peak of the Kids
Sìthean Mór	:	Large Fairy Hill
Sròn Bheag (Beag)	:	Small Headland

In pocket on inside back cover:
Map of Tertiary Igneous Complex of Ardnamurchan